Pocket Activity Guide

for Wiley Geography Textbooks and Microsoft® Encarta® Virtual Globe

Margaret M. Gripshover
Marshall University

Thomas L. Bell
The University of Tennessee, Knoxville

John Wiley & Sons, Inc.
New York • Chichester • Weinheim
Brisbane • Singapore • Toronto

ISBN 0-471-25409-6

Printed in the United States of America

10 9 8 7 6 5 4 3 2

Printed and bound by Courier Westford, Inc.

This volume is dedicated
to the memory of our fathers

Robert S. Gripshover
(1928-1975)

Walter S. Bell
(1908-1980)

Acknowledgements

The authors wish to express their sincere appreciation to our Editor, Nanette Kauffman, and Assistant Editor, Barbara Bredenko, for their cheerfulness, patience and goodwill throughout the entire process of bringing this volume from concept to completed product. It was really Nanette's vision that guided the process throughout and we hope we have been faithful to that vision of showcasing the incredible range of activities that one can accomplish using Microsoft® *Encarta*® *Virtual Globe CD-ROM*. The authors have become believers in the software product and are continually amazed by its flexibility and comprehensiveness. The decision to package the textual material with the CD-ROM and *Pocket Guide* for a very attractive add-on fee was a good one. If the proof of the pudding is in the tasting, we hope the proof of this software is its continued use as a valuable reference tool throughout the student's college career and beyond.

We also want to thank the geography departments at Marshall University and The University of Tennessee, Knoxville for providing us with space and resources to complete the project. Kyle Rector and Terry Gilhula, advanced graduate students in geography at Tennessee, deserve much thanks for making sure that the computers used in the project were installed properly and up-to-date.

Table of Contents

Introduction   xii

Part I: Activities for World Regional Geography   1
Back in the USSR: Georgia on My Mind   3
Von Thünen on Whole Wheat? Contemporary
    European Agricultural Land Use   5
Siberia: Many Rivers Run Through It   9
Uh Oh, Canada: A Fractured Federal Tale   11
The Land of Shake and Bake: Landscapes and
    Volcanoes in Mexico   14
Suriname: Going Dutch in the Rain Forest   17
Are Kurds in the Way? The Political Geography
    of Kurdistan   20
One Hump or Two? Overland Trade Routes to
    Timbuktu   22
The Untouchables: A Caste of Millions   25
Dragon China into the 21st Century   28
A Close Shave: Will Myanmar Ever Revert to
    Burma?   31
Australia Rocks!   35
Want to Know Samoa? Read On!   37

Part II: Activities for Human Geography   41
Rocky Mountain High (and Corn Belt Low)   43
You Are My Density   47
Like Salmon Swimming Upstream?   51
Not So Great (Life) Expectations   56
A Woman's Place is in the House…and in
    the Senate   61
What'll It be: Lethargic and Clever or
    Vigorous and Stupid?   64
You Are What You Speak: African
    Lingua Francae   68

Christianity Worldwide: Plain Vanilla or
    31 Flavors   71
Let Them Eat Jute: The Colonial Legacy in
    World Agriculture   74
Planet of the Apes? The Primate City Distribution 77
Maquiladora? Is That the Latest Latin
    Dance Craze?   81
The Yacht Sea People: Roll the Dice and End Up
    in Vancouver   84
Large Map, Small Scale; Small Map, Large Scale 89
Postcards from Encarta: Wish You Were Here!   93
Digging to Chinatown: Relocation Diffusion
    in Action   96
A Matter of Some Gravity: World Population Cores
    and Distance Decay   99
My Prism Can Be My Prison   104
Around the World from Pre- to Post-Industrial   108
Another Type of Egyptian Pyramid   112
Ecotourism: It Isn't Easy Being Green—But it
    Can Be Profitable   116
Towns in Iowa: Central Places and a Whole
    Lot More!   120
Manhattan Transformation: The Suburban Roots
    of Harlem   124
I'll See Your Bernadette Devlin and Raise You
    an Ian Paisley   127
Timor or Less: Indonesia's Claim at Stake   131
How Would You Like Your Animals—Rare?
    Vacancies at the World Zoo   134

Part III: Activities for Physical Geography   *137*
    Zoning in on Greenwich: Giving You the
        Time of Day   138

(Sing Along!) There's a Hole, There's a Hole,
   There's a Whole at the Bottom of the World:
   Ozone Depletion in Antarctica 141
Keeping Your Head Above Water: Sea Levels
   and Global Warming 144
Somewhere Over the Rain Shadow 147
A World Wind Tour 150
Gone With the Wind 153
Köppen, Schmerpen: How Can Botany Possibly
   Aid Climatology? 157
Don't Take All Rocks for Granite, It's
   Sedimentary, My Dear Student, or I Never
   Metamorphic I Didn't Like. 161
Continental Blue Plate Special Fetuccine
   Alfredo Wegener 163
Return to Cinder 165
Permafrosting on the Cake: Weathering in
   Arctic Regions 168
'Mites Go Up, 'Tites Come Down: Karst
   Sinkholes and Caves 170
Wet and Wild Waterfalls 173
That Canyon, Steve—It's a Butte! 176
Loess is More 179
The Iceman Misseth: Implications for
   Driftless Area 182
Our Just Deserts: Soil Erosion 185
Act Locally, Think Globally 187

Part IV: Activities for Economic Geography 191
One Picture Tells a Thousand Geographies
   (or Where's Wheeler?) 192
Painting the World By Numbers 194
Thumbs Down: A Hitchhiker's Guide to
   the Globe 197
Banking on Technology 200

ix

Geography is Very Spatial To Me! 203

The Root of the Canal System: Erie, Isn't It? 206

Houston, We Have a Problem: Invasion of
the Multiple Nuclei 208

Here's the Rub: The Dutch Have to Modify
Central Place Spacing 210

A Tale of Three Cities 213

Run for the Border: NAFTA 216

Diamond in the Rough: Facets of Industrial
Development 218

Hot Under the Crust: Geothermal Energy
in Iceland 220

"Real" Agriculture: Implosion or Explosion? 222

How Now, Dairy Cow? 226

Part V: Activities for Contemporary Europe 229

From Steel Girders to Fiber Optics: Origins of
the European Union 230

Alpine For You 234

A Grecian Formula for Population? The Graying
of Europe 236

Skirting the Issue: Mini or Micro States? 239

Oil and Water DO Mix: Petroleum Reserves
in the North Sea 243

How Did Brussels Sprout? Urbanization
in Belgium 246

Planting the Garden Cities of Tomorrow:
Avoiding Urban Anarchy in the UK 249

A Jug of Wine, A Loaf of Bread, and Encarta:
French Viticulture 253

Leaving Their Denmark: The Far-Flung Faeroes
Without Pyramids 257

Malta Milks Tourism 261

The Walls Came a Tumblin' Down: Will the
   Two Germanys Ever Be Truly United?   264
Krakow's Holocaust Legacy   268
Unhappily Ever After?   271

Part VI: Activities for Latin America and
      the Caribbean   275
Where Not to Be in Raincoat Sales: High and Dry
   in the Atacama Desert   276
Trail of Years: Historical Linkages Along The
   Inca Highway   278
Coca Puffs: Cracking Down on the Cocaine
   Trade   280
Why You Have to Go to New York City to Get
   Your Go-Go Boots Shined: Brazilians on the
   Move   282
Show Some Spine! Land Use in the Latin
   American City   285
The Tin Men and Women: Mining in Bolivia   288
Yúcantan if You Don't Wear Sunscreen:
   Tourism in the Land of the Maya   291
Roller Costa Rica: Riding the Wave of
   Prosperity   295
Volcanoes in the Lesser Antilles: Hot Time
   in the Islands   299
Mountains of Potatoes: The Nature and Cultures
   of the Andes   302
Were They Brazil Nuts? Brasilia in Retrospect   305
Don't Cry for Me Argentina: You Can't be
   Pompous about the Pampas   308
Banking on the Future of Latin America:
   Solving Rural Poverty   312

Index   315

Introduction

John Wiley and Sons, Inc., has entered into an exciting agreement with Microsoft® to package the latest version of Microsoft® *Encarta® Virtual Globe CD-ROM* with many popular Wiley undergraduate textbooks in geography. The idea is to offer the CD-ROM at a vastly discounted price over what the student might have to pay if he or she purchased the software separately. Virtual Globe is an interactive electronic atlas that combines traditional thematic maps with video clips, slides, sound clips, data sets and so much more. This *Pocket Guide for the Use of Encarta® Virtual Globe CD-ROM* is included with the software. We have prepared this *Pocket Guide* to provide faculty and students with a learning tool that connects the software with the material in the textbooks. Exercises or activities are included for each chapter (or section) of nine best-selling Wiley textbooks. These books include three introductory physical geography textbooks with approximately the same content sequencing (Strahler and Strahler 1997; Strahler and Strahler 1998; de Blij and Muller 1997), a regional geography textbook (deBlij and Muller 1996) and two human geography texts (de Blij 1996; Kuby, *et al.*, 1998). Activities using the *Encarta® Virtual Globe CD-ROM* were also developed for more specialized texts in economic geography (Wheeler, *et al.* 1998) and the regional geography of Latin America (Blouet and Blouet, 1996) and Europe (Berentsen, 1997).

We hope to engage students in a positive interactive experience rather than using Encarta as a place name memorization tool. We will have succeeded in our mission if the student feels compelled to incorporate the material from the *Virtual Globe CD-ROM* in other contexts beyond the particular course for which they first purchased it. And, for those students who are somewhat technophobic, the *Pocket Guide* will ease them into displaying data in both mapped and tabular form and drawing the appropriate conclusions from those data. Students may also take virtual field trips via wonderful slide sets, videos, and sound clips that can be accessed for various countries or themes. Some of the activities use a *measuring tool* that can be used to determine the straight line distance between any pair of nodes on a map produced at any given scale. Within the context of a given activity, the student might be asked to go to the *Web Links* associated with particular themes or areas. When connected by modem or Ethernet connection, the *Encarta® Virtual Globe CD-ROM* has a built-in browser (Microsoft® Internet Explorer) that catalogues relevant *Web Links*. The instructor may add to this list if he or she knows of relevant links that are not included. For example, in an activity that focuses on the "Great Migration" of African Americans from the rural South to the urban North, a Web link is included to a Library of Congress site. That site focuses specifically on the impact of the African American migration stream for the city of Chicago. The Web site references a current exhibition that highlights the black experience. Ephemeral Web sites can be a problem for anyone using the Internet as a teaching tool, but many of the Encarta® links that are pre-loaded into the CD-ROM are official sources or reputable and well-established commercial enterprises and are less likely to suddenly disappear.

What do the activities and exercises in the *Pocket Guide* consist of exactly? Each is relatively short (about 2-3 pages) with a focused set of questions the student could answer after he or she explores some highlighted aspect of the *Virtual Globe*. They may, for example, be asked to compare Bantu music with that of the Hausa using the *Sights and Sounds* feature. Or, they may be taken to a W*eb link* that describes the riches and delights of ancient Timbuktu and asked to compare the account with the modern situation of Timbouctou in Mali. Likewise, they may be asked to assess the mapped correlation between infant mortality rates and total fertility rate at the world scale using both maps and data arrayed in tabular form. Students can see for themselves the mistake that Dutch planners made by hewing too closely to the spacing requirements of Christaller's classic central place model when settlements were located on reclaimed polderlands. They might realize that rock(s) in Australia could refer to the sacred Ayres (Uluru) Rock of the aborigines, the place of first settlement in Sydney or the many internationally famous rock bands that have gotten their start in that country. At the end of each activity is a list of keywords that defines its regional and thematic content.

The Importance of the Index

These keywords are cross-referenced in an index so that the instructor is not limited to assigning activities from one textbook only. Suppose the instructor is interested in the cross-cultural comparison of urban spatial structure. He or she might have students examine the presentation of the Griffin-Ford model for the Latin American city in

Blouet and Blouet's Latin American textbook as well as the coverage of the restructured metropolis in Wheeler, *et al.* regarding the North American city.

System Requirements and a Few Suggestions

The *Encarta® Virtual Globe CD-ROM* is designed to run in a Microsoft® Windows environment (NT 4.0 or later, or Windows 95 or later) and must have at least 8 MBs of RAM available although it works most efficiently with a full 32 MBs of RAM available.

Encarta® Virtual Globe is at its most useful when speakers and a sound card are part of the computer's configuration. It can be used without sound (a warning message to that effect is posted) but there are many musical clips and other sounds that add to the overall enjoyment of the software.

The software must **be installed** the first time that *Encarta®* is inserted into a machine that has not previously played the software. This takes only about a minute, but might seem quite daunting to the student who has never used this type of computer software before. Every school and university system will be configured differently, but it would behoove the instructor to make sure that the software is actually installed on all the computers that the student might have access to avoid any unnecessary glitches or delays. We want students to be intrigued, not frustrated. And they will be with minimum guidance. The software is very logically constructed and "forgiving". By the latter term we mean that there may be several routes that can be taken to achieve a desired end. It may even be advisable to devote one period just for students to "play" with the features of the CD-ROM in a group setting (e.g., a computer laboratory). There is a synergistic effect that will reverberate throughout the room and excite even the seemingly uninterested student in a way that other media cannot.

Features that Students will Undoubtedly Discover on Their Own

There are features of the CD-ROM that are not included in our activities. For example, there is a built-in "Name that Place" geography quiz that may be played by an individual or perhaps by persons competing against each other. There are five levels of expertise in this game and the twenty questions that comprise a round are randomly generated. For those who enjoy *Jeopardy!* or *Trivial Pursuit*, this game will be addictive.

Likewise, there are several *world flights* included in the software that allow the student "pilot" to fly over a particular corridor and view the landscape below. Only a few of these flight paths have been used in the *Pocket Guide* activities, but the instructor may wish to incorporate more as he or she sees fit. The instrument controls may be adjusted to fly lower or higher, more slowly or more rapidly or in a changed direction if desired. Students will probably discover the delights of this feature of *Encarta® Virtual Globe* on their own. We hope your students will enjoy *Encarta® Virtual Globe CD-ROM* and that the accompanying *Pocket Guide* that we have written will save you valuable exercise preparation time. Have fun!

Part One

Activities
for *World Regional Geography*
Using Encarta®
Virtual Globe

Back in the USSR: Georgia on My Mind

Typically, most geographic realms are easily identified through their marked and distinguished boundaries. (See illustration I-1 in your text.) For instance, regions such as North America, South America, Australia, and even parts of East and South Asia are easily recognizable. But what about areas with less distinct boundaries such as the three transition zones on perimeter of the North Africa/Southwest Asia realm? Where are these areas and why are they areas identified as "transition zones?" Two of these zones border Russia and continue to be influenced by decades of Soviet rule. During this time, the Soviet government exerted social and economic influence over these regions, attempting to culturally dilute the indigenous populations by resettling ethnic Russians within the territories.

To gain a better insight of the complexity of transition zones, take a closer look at the Trans-Caucasus. Using *Find*, create of map of the region by searching for Caucasus Mountains. Three former Soviet republics, Armeian, Azerbaijan, and Georgia, are now independent states. But, there are conflicts among these states stemming from religious, ethnic, linguistic, and cultural differences. One area of contention between Armenia and Azerbaijan is a territory called Nagorno-Karabakh. Click on *Geography* and use *Encarta's narrative* to describe in your own words the nature of this territorial dispute.

For each of the three newly independent states, use *Facts and Figures* to find the proportion of the population that adheres to various religions. Do you think that the fact that the vast majority of Armenians are Christian (i.e., Armenian Orthodox) and the vast majority of Azeris (i.e., residents of Azerbaizan) are Muslim could be one of the sources of irritation in their territorial dispute over Nogorno-Karabakh? Why or why not?

Can you name the President of Georgia? Click on *Society*. Then click on *Government*. What interesting linkages are there between the government of the former Soviet Union and the independent Republic of Georgia? What position did the current President of Georgia hold during the Soviet period?

Using *Facts and Figures*, compare the economy of Georgia with those of Russia and Turkey. Use Turkey as a representative of many of the countries in the North Africa/Southwest Asia realm. In what ways is the economic structure of Georgia closer to that of Russia? In what ways is it closer to that of Turkey?

Keywords: transition zone, Russia, Transcaucasus, Georgia, Armenia, Azerbaijan

Von Thünen on Whole Wheat? Contemporary European Agricultural Land Use

One of the classic location theories is that of the German economist Johann Heinrich von Thünen. Von Thünen was a brilliant scholar who contributed to the field of microeconomics with his notions about marginal returns to investment. In addition, he was a very successful gentlemen farmer who owned a large estate called Tellow in northern Germany near the present day city of Rostock. His principles of agriculture were developed from is own observations about farming and how much fertilizer, seed, etc., would reap the maximum production.

Von Thünen's theory was presented in his book *The Isolated State* written in 1826 and fully translated into English in 1966. Von Thünen wrote his theory at a time when transportation from his farm to market was limited overland to carts drawn by draft animals. Thus, the geographic range at which the theory was applicable was limited in size. Modern geographers agree on von Thünen's basic principles that the distance from market determines the agricultural use of land and, similarly, land use intensity diminishes with greater distance from the market. Since modern analysis is on a much greater scale than von Thünen imagined, these models are sometimes referred to as macro-Thünen models. One such model is presented in your textbook (Figure 1-4, p. 53). In the previous figure (Figure 1-3, p. 52), the hypothetical land use pattern shown uses predicted by the purely economic principles developed by von Thunen in the absence of topographic barriers or place-to-place differences in soil fertility. Figure 1-4 is based on the yields of eight leading crops and was produced by van Valkenburg and Held many decades ago. In the 1960s, studies of agricultural land uses in Europe were updated, but is the pattern shown in Figure 1-4 still relevant in the 1990s?

One might argue that with the advent of the European Union, and the reduction of tariff barriers on agricultural products among the member states, that agriculture in Europe will begin to specialize to a much greater degree than in the past. Using the statistics available on *Encarta Virtual Globe*, let's see if the land use patterns presented in
 Figure 1-4 are still in evidence. Let's choose four countries that fall wholly or mostly within the hypothesized agricultural zone. Intensive farming and dairying may be represented by Denmark, the forest zone by Germany, field crops by Hungary, and ranching and animal products by Spain. Using *Map Styles*, select *Statistical*. Under the *Choose Statistics* option, select category *Agriculture and World Stats* for four representative crops or land uses.

For intensive farming and dairying let's use *Livestock, Cattle 1991*. In Europe, most cattle serve the dual purpose of providing dairy products and meat. In a larger country that can afford the luxury of agricultural specialization like the United States, some breeds (e.g., Holsteins, Jerseys, Guernseys)

6

have been bred for milk production almost exclusively and others (e.g., Angus, shorthorns) for meat production. You will probably wish to sort the data in the table alphabetically and look at the four countries in question.

For the forest zone, focus on two different statistics: within *Agriculture*, look at *Land-use area, forest and woodland, 1994* and within *Economics*, look at *Roundwood production, 1991*. Repeat the procedure. Why do you think that there is a discrepancy between the proportion of total land in a country devoted to forest and woodland and the actual harvesting of those woodlands for lumber (e.g., roundwood)?

For field crops let's choose *Wheat produced, 1994* under *Agriculture*. Maize (corn) does not grow well in Europe due to the lack of intensive insolation. But, Europe grows many short grain crops, such as rye, and tuber crops, such as potatoes, that have short growing seasons and can be planted in the poorer soils of northern Europe and the Scandinavian peninsula.

For the grazing of animals let's use *Livestock, sheep 1994* under *Agriculture* as sheep and goats can be pastured on poorer quality forage than can cattle and might more likely be found in agriculturally marginal areas. Do the statistics support the contention that the zones shown in Figure 1-4 are still relevant in the 1990s? That is, does Denmark rank relatively higher in cattle production than Hungary or Spain? How about sheep production in Spain? Is it relatively more important to the economy of that country than Hungary or Denmark? If you only consider the four

7

countries of interest (i.e., if you examine their rank relative to each other and not to all the other countries of the world) is the model of van Valkenberg and Held (Figure 1-4) still valid? Why or why not?

Keywords: Europe, von Thünen, model, agricultural land use

Siberia: Many Rivers Run Through It

Siberia means many things to many people, most of which are extremes. When winter weather turns frigid, meteorologists often liken the weather to Siberia. Imagine living in Noril'sk, the Siberian city whose major claim to fame is being the coldest city in the world with mean annual temperature of 12 degrees Fahrenheit. For centuries, Russian governments have exiled political prisoners and convicted criminals to Siberia since escapes through thousands of miles of desolate territory were nearly impossible. Basically, anything harsh, vast, bitterly cold, or Doctor Zhivago-like, has been associated with Siberia.

Siberia comprises a tremendous amount of territory in north-central Russia--over five million square miles of some of the most inhospitable land on the planet. Yet, Siberia is home to nearly 40 million residents. To locate Siberia, create a map using the *Find Places* icon. Among the most striking physical features are the three major rivers that drain the region. What are these rivers and what is significant about their direction of flow? There are over 150,000 streams in Siberia: all of which flow into the Arctic Ocean. How does this relate to the presence of extensive tundra bogs and poorly drained regions? Another important water feature in Siberia is Lake Baikal. Locate the lake on the map and find out what makes this body of water so unique. Change the *Map*

Style to *Physical*, then select *Ecoregions* for more information on habitats and climate. You may also want to view the slide show in *Sights and Sounds* to see examples of the region's natural and cultural landscape. Did you know that reindeer are the world's only domesticated deer? Would you want to live in the village depicted in the *Life in Siberia* slide? To find out the ethnic heritage of Siberian folk music, listen to the samples titled *Russia: Sakha Music* and *Russia: Shaman Music*. You can use the slide show to learn more about natural resource exploitation in fragile tundra environments.

What may surprise you most about Siberia is the level of economic and cultural development in a region lacking in transportation routes and inhabited by far-flung settlements. Use *Web Links* to further explore Siberia. Take a *Virtual Tour of Siberia* or travel through the region on *Russia's Trans-Siberian Railway*. Live the life of an urban Siberian resident by clicking on the *Novosibirsk--The Capital of Siberia Web Link*. And for some Siberian culture, visit the *SibArtNet* and enjoy art gallery displays of contemporary Siberian art.

Now, don't you think Siberia is cool--in more ways than one?

Keywords: Siberia Tundra Folk Music Trans-Siberian Railroad Novosibirsk

Uh Oh, Canada:
A Fractured Federal Tale

Canada is a country facing incredible challenges
from within and beyond its borders. United States
residents outnumber Canadians nearly ten to one.
Since the vast majority of Canadians live within 100
miles of the U.S. border, it is nearly impossible for
them to escape U.S. media and cultural influences.
Canada is the United States' number one trading
partner. Canada, however, is not simply an arctic
version of the United States and while it struggles to
maintain an individual identity within the North
American realm, it is also in deep turmoil over
internal problems. Among the most difficult issues
facing Canadians today is ethnic division manifested
in the separatist movements of two different groups.
First, the residents of the province of Quebec, known
as the Quebecois, and, secondly, the Inuit of the
Northwest Territories--a people formerly and
erroneously identified with other northern tribal
groups and referred to as Eskimos. After these two
groups you should consider the following question:
What do the Quebecois and Inuit have in common
and how have the goals of these groups affected the
federal integrity of Canada?

Quebec
In 1995, the Quebecois narrowly defeated a
referendum to separate from Canada. What forces
would bring about such a drastic measure? In

comparison, could you imagine the consequences if Iowa would decide to separate from the United States? To learn more about the historical background that provoked the separatist vote, use *Find Countries* to create a map of Canada and click on *Quebec*. Select *Geography* and read about the role of French as well as First Americans (i.e., what people in the United States call native Americans) in the development of Quebec. For additional details on the province's physical geography, history, culture, and economic development, go to *Web Links* and select *Canadian Provinces and Territories*. Did you know that the Appalachian Mountains extend into Quebec? Describe the pattern of immigration to Quebec since the 1960s. How might this impact the future of Quebec? To get the true flavor of French culture, click on *Sights and Sounds*. Try *Quebecois Cuisine* and listen to a music sample with *Canada: French Song*.

Northwest Territories/Nunavut

The struggles of the Quebecois to retain and protect their cultural identity are well known but what of another influential minority group in Canada—First Americans? Canada's nearly 350,000 First Americans include, among others, Mohawk, Cree, Algonquin, Huron, and Inuit. Of these groups, the Inuit have been politically successful in securing a homeland while most others live on reservations throughout Canada. In 1999, the Inuit will take control of a large eastern section of the Northwest Territories known as Nunavut. Let's take a closer look at this part of Canada and its people. Go to a map of Canada and click on *Northwest Territories*. Get some background information on the Territories by clicking on *Geography*. Where do you find the majority of population? Who are the Dene and metis? Why is the new territory for the Inuit being called Nunavut? While you are exploring the Northwest Territories, check out the *Web Links* for the *Prince of Wales Northern Heritage Center*. Follow the links to the *Introduction* page and scan down to the *Research Room*. Select *Northern Vignettes* and explore the cultural heritage of the region. Learn how the Pelly Bay Stone Church was built with canvas, seal oil, and ashes, which were hauled to the site by dogsled teams. To take a closer look at the new territory, use *Find Places* and enter *Nunavut*. This will give you a map showing the location of the new Inuit homeland. Go to *Web Links* and click on *The Nunatsiaq News* homepage. Read the news from an Inuit point of view, especially those articles that deal with the future of Nunavut.

Keywords: Canada, Quebec, Northwest Territories, Nunavut, Ethnicity, Separatists, Culture, Quebecois, Inuit

The Land of Shake and Bake: Landscapes of Earthquakes and Volcanoes in Mexico

Would you locate a city on an almost unbuildable location because of your belief in a myth? The Aztecs did. The site for their capital of Tenóchtitlan was selected because of a legend that wherever an eagle with a serpent in its beak landed on a cactus that would be the ideal mystical site for their capital. Unfortunately, that cactus was growing on a reed and mud island in the middle of a large fresh water lake, Lake Texcoco. The symbolism of the eagle with the serpent on a cactus is still a powerful one in Mexico; it is depicted on their peso coin and on their flag.

Present day Mexico City is located right on top of the Aztec capital. In fact, when digging for an extension of Mexico City's subway system, workers discovered the base of an important ceremonial pyramid from the Aztec era. That stonework has been preserved next to a modern Mexican marketplace and a Spanish colonial-era church at the Plaza De Los Tres Culturas (Plaza of the Three Cultures—Aztec or Indian, Spanish and modern Mexican). Each of those three cultureq has shaped and reshaped this modern, bustling city in central Mexico. Locate this important Plaza by using the *Find Places* command and bringing up a map of Mexico City.

While the site of Mexico City may have been ill-advised, its situation—the location relative to important trade routes and its centrality as a hub of communication and transportation within the nation is unparalleled.

How ill-advised was the site of present day Mexico City? Although the important tourist attraction of the floating gardens of Xochimilco is about all that remains of ancient Lake Texcoco, the legacy of locating a city on a lake bed of rather recent sedimentary deposition remains. Click on *Mexico* and choose *Sights and Sounds*. There you will see the Palace of the Fine Arts building as it has sunk over 15 feet since construction. It is said that the foundation of the Latin American Towers Building (over 41 stories in height and, at one time, the tallest building in Mexico) extends almost as deeply below ground in order to reach the firmer bedrock beneath the lakebed sediments.

Unfortunately, not all buildings in rapidly growing Mexico City (the most populated and polluted city in North America) are as soundly constructed as the Latin American Towers. Why is this a problem? Click on *Mexico* and choose the *Map Style* labeled *Physical* and the extension labeled *Tectonic*. Tectonic activity is mountain building activity most commonly associated with earthquakes and volcanoes. Mexico City is near the convergence of crustal plates. Movements along these fault lines have had a devastating recent impact on Mexico City. In 1985, the strongest earthquake recorded in recent years (an 8.2 on the Richter scale), had an epicenter some 200 miles from Mexico City. Because of the inherent geological instability of the lake sediments upon which Mexico City stands, the shock waves from that earthquake leveled many buildings in Mexico City, killing and injuring thousands of people. It was as if Mexico City were sitting in a bowl (i.e., the Basin of Mexico) filled with jelly (i.e., unconsolidated lake sediments). According to the *Tectonic* map, how many crustal plates are near Mexico City? Is it any wonder that the city has received and continues to receive many earth tremors? What part of Mexico is even more earthquake-prone than central Mexico?

Click on *Sights and Sounds* of Mexico and focus on the view of Mexico City presented there. What do you notice in the distance? That's right. There are two snow-covered mountains beyond the lower mountains that form the Basin of Mexico. These two mountains are of volcanic origin. Click once again on the *Find* function and look up the information for Volcan Iztaccihuatl and Volcan Popocatepetl. These place names are long and difficult for us to pronounce because they are in the language of the Aztecs, not that of the Spanish conquistadores. How does Iztaccihuatl translate? Do you think that it is an appropriate place name? Why or why not?

Keywords: Mexico, Mexico City, earthquakes, volcanoes

Suriname:
Going Dutch in the Rain Forest

The dominant colonial forces for the majority of South America were the Spanish and the Portuguese except on the northeast coast of the continent in a region known today as the "Three Guianas." The Three Guianas include Guyana, French Guiana and Suriname. Only French Guiana remains under colonial rule as a French department. Guyana was ruled by the British and gained independence in 1966. Suriname was a Dutch colony and has been an independent state since 1975. Of the three, we will focus on Suriname. Suriname has a complex cultural heritage as a result of European, African, and Asian immigration with many of those belonging to the latter two groups--descendents of slaves or indentured servants. In addition to social complexities, Suriname faces serious economic and environmental challenges that are highly interrelated and difficult to reconcile given the country's political and monetary instability.

What makes the Three Guianas unique in South America is that they are more similar in character to islands in the Caribbean than with their Latin American neighbors. One of the best ways to learn about this complex country is to explore the *Web Links* for Suriname. In particular, you need to check out the *Tropical Rainforest in Suriname* link. Let's go there and answer some questions about this

17

fascinating country. Create a map of Suriname and click on *Web Links*. Select the *Rainforest* site and prepare to take a multimedia tour of the Suriname rainforest. There are a variety of images and sounds on this site as you visit Suriname and its rainforest. An excellent companion to the web page is *Sights and Sounds for Suriname* as well as the *Animals* link. Okay, let's take a virtual tour of Suriname.

For example, how has the lack of transportation infrastructure affected economic development in the Three Guianas? Could you drive your car from Paramaribo to Caracas? What is the lingua franca of Suriname, what are its roots and when did it develop? What does a swampen en ritsen in Suriname have in common with the landscape of the Netherlands? How is the savanna different from the climate along the coastal plain? Would you want to take a drink from a "Cola" creek? Who are the Arowaks and Caribs and which group invented a sailing ship? What sort of houses do Amerindians build? What type of "brew" might you enjoy with Galibi smoked fish. Given the region's climate, are you surprised to find bauxite deposits here?

Bauxite has long provided Suriname with a major export product, but how has aluminum refining affected Maroon villages in the rainforest? Who are the Maroons and what role have they played in our understanding of rainforest ecosystems? One of the major reasons why the rainforest is threatened has been the exhaustion of once extensive bauxite deposits. The Suriname government has shifted its economic development emphasis from bauxite mining to logging and gold mining. What have been the environmental consequences of these alternative economic initiatives? What types of flora and fauna do you find in the Suriname rainforest? Should visitors be warned about tortoises falling out of trees? What type of plant could be described as the rainforest's "trash can?"

There is much more to learn about Suriname. Be sure to check out other *Web Links* as well as *Society* and *Facts and Figures* to increase your understanding of this unique country and its neighbors within South America. And watch where you step. There might be a *Teraphusa leblondi* in your path!

Keywords: Suriname, Three Guianas, rainforest, colonialism, Amerindians

Are Kurds in the Way?
The Political Geography of Kurdistan

Before you begin this activity, study the map displayed in Figure 6-12 (p. 301) and the accompanying story about a homeland for the Kurds on the following page. It is clear from the book's discussion that there are major differences between a nation and a state. In your own words, state what these differences are (refer to pp.56-57 in the text for further insight).

We've learned that the Kurds are "fractious and fragmented", but who are they really? What is their ethnic, cultural, religious and linguistic background? Why, like the Basques on the border region between Spain and France, do they want their own autonomous state?

The textbook introduces the Kurdish people and their plight, but we really don't know much about the Kurds themselves. Use the *Find* command and *Content* as the aspect you wish to focus on to bring up any material that might exist on the Kurds. Where is their traditional cultural hearth located? Hint: Note the slide of Lake Van in eastern Turkey in *Sights and Sounds*. The lake is saline and contains many other minerals as well. This area appears to be the traditional core of their culture realm. Look at the map in the textbook of the disputed region and find the Kurdish core area (Figure 6-12 on p. 301).

The Kurds traditionally lived in rather isolated mountainous villages in the area now occupied by portions of Iran, Iraq, Turkey, Syria, and Azerbaijan. Why is the 36th parallel shown on the map in the Kurdish area of Iraq? Before the Gulf War, Kurds were located throughout the Iraqi region of Kordestan. Click on *Kordestan* and find out what makes the region so valuable? In the description of Kurdistan, what is mentioned specifically about the Zagros Mountains that form the southeastern border of the region that the Kurds would like to make their autonomous homeland? How important is this resource in making the states that have significant Kurdish minorities reticent to give up land to create such a new state?

Do the Kurds have their own separate language and culture? Click on *Sights and Sounds* and take an *Afternoon Break in Sanli Urfa, Turkey*. Now visit the Kurdish Village in *Sights and Sounds*. Both the Iranians and the Kurds are followers of Muhammad the Prophet. How, then, do they differ in religious practice? See if you can find a site on the Encarta CD-ROM or a suggested Web site that would briefly explain the difference between the Sunni (Kurdish) and Shi'ite (Iranian) branches of Islam.

What happened in 1979 to make the Iranians more hostile to the demands for Kurdish autonomy? (Hint: check for *Society* under the heading Iran)

Keywords: Kurds, Iran, Iraq, Turkey, state, nation

One Hump or Two?
Overland Trade Routes to Timbuktu

Recently, biologists are reticent to call the one-humped "ship of the Sahara" a camel, preferring instead the name Dromendary. The term camel is instead reserved for the two-humped Bactrian variety found in the drier portions of central Asia. Both types have been important beasts of burden during an era when roads were nonexistent. Even today there the Sahara of northern Africa that can only be crossed by these animals that can store water for prolonged periods in their hump(s).

One of the early outposts that stirred the collective imaginations of Europeans was exotic and inaccessible Timbuktu (now spelled Tombouctou). The name itself connoted an air of mystery and excitement. Despite its interior location in landlocked Mali, it was the nexus of an extensive trade network and a major center of Islamic learning. Using the *Find* command, bring up a map of the Tombouctou area. Note the pattern of highways and land routes into and out of the city. Geographers often refer to such a pattern as a hub-and-spoke system. If Tombouctou is the hub, where do the "spokes" leading to the north and northeast end up? These are the remnants of the camel caravan routes that brought Tombouctou such wealth and fame at the height of its importance in the fifteenth and sixteenth centuries. So even though it is located in the Sahel and not Subsaharan African, its influences extended far south into the interior of the African continent.

If water is so important to sustain life, why is Tombouctou situated some twelve miles from the nearest branch of the Niger River? Perhaps an early account of a visit to Timbuktu might help to answer some of these questions. Click on *Web Links* and scroll down to a document entitled *Leo Africanus: Description of Timbuktu (1526)*. Even reading about the personal history of the man who wrote the narrative is interesting. He was a Moorish slave freed by Pope Leo X and is reputed to have written this account in Italian and, at the end of his life, renounced Christianity and reconverted to Islam.

Even if portions of this travel dialog are exaggerated as the endnotes suggest, such travel accounts formed the basis for the European stereotypical view of such exotic places at a time when travel was severely limited to all but the very rich.

How does El Hasan ben Muhammed el-Wazzan-ez-Zayyati (a.k.a. Johannis Leo de Medici) explain the site of Timbuktu so far from a source of fresh flowing water? Does the manner in which the king dealt with his defeated enemies in battle surprise you? Where do you think these unfortunate victims of war--or those refusing to offer monetary tribute to the king--ended up?

In beginning economics classes, salt is often used as an example of a good that is relatively price inelastic.

Since salt is an essential ingredient for human existence, at least in small quantities, the price of salt could double and our demand for the product would not diminish appreciably. We are simply fortunate to live in a place where salt is relatively abundant and inexpensive. Where do you think the source of salt needed by the residents of Timbuktu was located? Would the use of camels have been involved in this trade as well?

Finally, click on the *Web Link* entitled *Images of the Changing Sahel* showing changes in the Niger River floodplain in the Sahel of Africa, near Tombouctou. In the ten year period from 1976 to 1985, how would you describe the environmental degradation (i.e., desertification) that has taken place in the region? Do you think that Tombouctou still contains "many wells containing sweet water?" When the Niger floods do you think it is still true that "canals deliver water to the city?" Why or why not?

Keywords: Timbuktu (Tombouctou), Mali, camels, trade routes

The Untouchables:
A Caste of Millions

The Indian subcontinent is the birthplace of
Hinduism, Buddhism, Sikhism, and Jainism. But by
far, the religion most closely associated with India is
Hinduism. Nearly 80 percent of India's population
of almost one billion are believers in Hinduism. To
understand Indian history and contemporary society
one must explore the role of religion in the country's
unity and internal conflict.

Hinduism is an ethnic religion practiced mainly in
India. Hinduism has spread throughout the world
mainly through immigration. Hindus do not seek
converts as do other religions such as Islam and
Christianity. Hinduism is also closely linked to
social stratification within India due to the caste
system. Castes are a Hindu system of social rank
based on ancestry, family relationships, and vocation.
Hindus believe in reincarnation and thus the caste
you are born into is reflective of your actions in a
previous life. The most prestigious caste members
are the Brahmans and the lowest caste is the
untouchables. Traditionally, untouchables have
been the poorest of the poor, socially, politically, and
economically ostracized by upper caste members.
The plight of the untouchables compelled British
colonial rulers and subsequent Indian governments to
attempt to improve the lives of millions of these
lowest caste members.

Let's travel to India to learn how Hinduism creates the social backdrop for India's Hindu majority population. Create a map of India using the *Find Countries* tool. Take a moment and read *Society* to see how Hinduism influences many aspects of life in India from religious practices to politics. How has the interpretation of the caste system changed over time? Given India's political and economic climate, what do you see as the future for the untouchables? What might be the fate of other religious factions in India? In recent times, why have Hindus and Muslims been involved in violent conflicts?

India is not the only Asian country with large percentages of its population as practicing Hindus. Hinduism has spread from the subcontinent to bordering countries and beyond. For each of India's neighbors, identify which religions have the most followers using *Facts and Figures*. Be sure to include Sri Lanka in your search. You may be surprised to discover that there is actually a bordering country with a higher percentage of Hindus than India. Which country is this and why do you think this pattern has emerged? When you figure out which of India's neighbors this is, check out *Sights and Sounds*, in particular *Gaines Music* and the *Caste System of the Newar*. Where else can you find Hinduism playing and important societal roles beyond the borders of India? For two examples, go to Mauritius and Bali and select *Sights and Sounds*. For Mauritius, select the slide for *Hindu Dominance* and for Bali click on *Seaside Offering*. How did Hinduism diffuse to these locations? Can you find other countries outside the South Asian realm with significant numbers of Hindus? Do you think Hinduism plays the same role in these countries as it does in India?

Keywords: India, Hinduism, caste system, untouchables, diffusion, religion

Dragon China into the 21st Century

Some China watchers suggest that the greatest economic power of the 21st century will be the People's Republic of China. The United States has only one-fourth the number of people and although its rate of economic growth is the envy of many developed nations in Europe and elsewhere it is much slower than that of China. China has a long way to go. It has come from a backward peasant society under the thumb of feudal warlords at the beginning of this century through the worst "cleansing" excesses of the Communist regime--the Red Guard, the "Gang of Four" and the cult of Mao-- to what it is today. China is still a Communist regime, but is poised to become a major player on the world's economic stage if not its political equivalent.

China doesn't come close to the egalitarian ideal of a socialist worker's paradise. The income levels among the provinces vary greatly. Those to the south, especially those near the newly acquired "province" of Hong Kong, are growing very rapidly as are the fast growing coastal provinces along the Pacific Rim. In contrast, many interior provinces suffer great poverty and practice much more of a traditional agricultural peasant economy.

One of the brightest stars on China's horizon is the economically alluring city of Shanghai and its surrounding region. Shanghai has always been the largest and most important city when it comes to foreign trade. With a bustling port and excellent supporting infrastructure, Shanghai truly is China's gateway and entrepôt to the rest of the world. Click on *Find* and bring up the map of the area around Shanghai. What factors contribute to the excellence of its site and situation? Reportedly, almost 25 percent of the world's construction cranes are located in Shanghai proper and the area of Pudong, located on the opposite bank of the Huangpo River (i.e., Jiang). What are they building? Check the latest for yourself. Click on to *Web Links* for Shanghai and examine *A Look at Shanghai*. More specifically focus on the section entitled *What's New?* which gives a thumbnail sketch of all the major new construction projects in the surrounding region.

Why is this city that was referred to as the "Paris of the Orient" in the 1920s re-experiencing such phenomenal growth? Shanghai was, and always will be, well positioned in the increasingly global trade. In the 1920s, the Bund, a government and shopping district on the waterfront, was the place to see and to be seen. Click on *Sights and Sounds* to see for yourself *Shanghai Shoppers on the Bund*. The legacy of the "Golden Age" of European power in this area of China can be seen it the ornate facades of some of the older buildings along the Bund and elsewhere. For a photographic display of some of the best examples of turn-of-the century European colonial architecture and comparisons with traditional Chinese buildings click on the *Web Links* and examine the site called *Shanghai's Historical Western Architecture*. The black and white photographs of the Shanghai are stunning.

Much of the foreign investment in Shanghai is made by Chinese financiers living overseas. These expatriates are Chinese people whose families fled mainland China when the Communists took over in 1949. This huge migration, by some estimates the greatest the world has ever known, is sometimes referred to as the Chinese diaspora or scattering. Chinese people then reestablished themselves throughout East and Southeast Asia and around the world. The hard driving economy of Singapore, experiencing the first real downturn in their economies at the time of this writing, is largely controlled by these overseas Chinese expatriates. Persons of Chinese extraction from as far away as Vancouver or New York are flocking to Shanghai to invest in real estate ventures, start new businesses and build the industrial and service infrastructure necessary for Shanghai to emerge as a truly global city to rival Tokyo, London or New York. The investment is often made through tight-knit family organizations called guang-xi. These investment groups are largely closed to outside investors which has created suspicion and jealousy among entrepreneurs who feel they are being excluded from some lucrative opportunities. Outside investors argue that to be of Chinese ancestry gives one advantage in this globally competitive Chinese market. Do you think that such family-owned business arrangements are much different than limited partnerships in the United States and elsewhere? Why or why not?

Keywords: China, Shanghai, guang-xi, overseas Chinese

A Close Shave: Will Myanmar Ever Revert to Burma?

Myanmar (Burma) is one of the poorest, least Westernized countries that is run by one of the most oppressive military regimes in all of Southeast Asia. On the other hand, it is one of the most spiritual and beautiful places on Earth. Myanmar has consciously turned its back on the modern world and cut off all contact with the West. In turn, the military regime that came to power in 1988 (the State Law and Order Restoration Council--SLORC) continues to defy the will of the Burmese people. At first, it was thought that this military regime might right the corruption that was rampant throughout the country. Bribery and scandal was even tainting the Buddhist monks. Elections were called for in 1990 and despite there being 93 parties running--many representing small ethnic minority groups that live near the border regions with China and Thailand--the National League for Democracy (NLD) won an overwhelming majority of the vote. The military regime refused to recognize that the people had spoken in this election and jailed many of the members of the NLD. Click on *Myanmar* or *Burma* using the *Find Countries* tool. Go to *Web Links* for Burma and examine the *Destination Myanmar* travel guide prepared by the British Lonely Planet travel agency. They call Myanmar "a bizarre, inept Orwellian society that has withdrawn from contact with the late 20th century". Although George Orwell actually did write a book based on his experience in Burma, it is likely that the

31

quotation refers to his more famous novel, *1984*. What, in your opinion, is an Orwellian society?

Now, go to the web site entitled *Project Burma* which keeps track of articles referring to human rights abuses in Myanmar and focus on the section dealing with Burma-US Relations. Who is the outspoken advocate for civil rights in Burma that won the Nobel Peace Prize for her efforts?

It may seem incongruous that such a politically repressed society is also a very spiritual one. The focus of most lives is the Buddhist religion and the center of a settlement's life is the monastery and the pagoda(s) dedicated to The Enlightened One. The main pagoda in Yangon (Rangoon), the capital and largest city, is covered with gold leaf. That Shwedogon Paya pagoda (temple) is alleged to contain eight hairs from the head of the Buddah. The form of Buddhism practiced in Burma differs from that practiced in Tibet or in China. Using *Web Links* examine the subject of religion in *Encarta On-line*. What type of Buddhism is practiced in Burma? What other countries also practice the same type? This link has a lot of information of the history of the people of Burma and is well worth reading in its entirety.

Next to petroleum and natural gas, Burma depends on tourism as its most important source of hard currency. The year 1996 was even declared the year to "Visit Myanmar" in official governmental policy. It's interesting to compare the tourist attractions felt worthy of a visit in an official source with those deemed viewable in a more "objective" non-governmental source. We'd like you to click on the

Web Link for *Welcome to Myanmar*, for an official
source of governmental propaganda on tourism.
Then examine *Destination Myanmar* developed by
the British travel group, the Lonely Planet. Both are
colorful and filled with pictures. One of the funniest
is found on the Lonely Planet's Web site. The
photograph is called "Cheroot vendor". Just what do
you suppose that woman is smoking!? At the Web
site you'll learn the Burmese like to drink tepid weak
green tea and chew betel. What exactly is betel?

Practically all of the tourist sites listed in the official
site are religious pagodas, many associated with
ancient capitals or centers of earlier civilization.
None of the buildings left from the British colonial
era, even the famous Strand Hotel in Rangoon
(Yangon) are mentioned in the official tourist source.
Seemingly more important are ancient capitals such
as Bagan. See if you can find that city on the map of
Burma. It is on the eastern bank of the Irrawaddy
(Ayeyarwaddy) River, a city of four million pagodas.
Another exotic location was made famous by a book
entitled *The Road to Mandalay* by Rudyard Kipling
and made even more so by the trio of Dorothy
Lamour, Bing Crosby and Bob Hope in a movie of
the same name. Mandalay was declared the capital
by King Mindon in 1857 because the Lord Buddah
prophesized that a great city would be founded at the
foot of Mandalay Hill. Today, Mandalay is the
second largest city in the country of Burma and
contains many important pagodas (temples) too. The
official guide implies that these tourist destinations
are easy to get to by air or road. The Lonely Planet is
more sanguine. Burma doesn't have an all-weather
road that traverses the country from north to south.

Internal air travel is unreliable as schedules change without notice. If visitors want to go upcountry by boat, they will have to rent a "tourist boat" at ten times the cost of a local boat which are supposedly off limits to tourists. No cruise ships are allowed into Myanmar at all. Travel in Burma appears to be for the adventurous.

As befits a lesser developed economy, over seventy percent of the gainfully employed labor force are in the extractive industries—agriculture, forestry, fishing, and mining. Rice is the main agricultural staple, but one should not overlook the fact that 60 to 80 percent of the heroin in the United States originates in the Golden Triangle portion of Myanmar at the border with Thailand, China and Laos. The farmer receives only about $700 a kilo for the unrefined heroin derived from opium poppies. By the time it is refined in Bangkok that kilo is worth $10,000. And, when that kilo hits the streets of New York City, its value has ballooned to $750,000. Incidentally, don't travel in that section of the country northeast of Mandalay. The warlord who controls the drug trafficking has bribed government officials to turn a blind eye to these goings-on and his own army of 15,000 troops are very xenophobic and quite well-armed.

Keywords: Myanmar (Burma), Yangon (Rangoon), Mandalay, Buddhism

Australia Rocks!

Diamonds from the Kimberly Plateau aren't the only rocks that you find in Australia. While rich in mineral wealth, Australia could draw on a variety of rocks to symbolize its history and culture.

Rock That Doesn't Roll: Uluru Rock
Uluru Rock, formerly known as Ayers Rock, is a major tourist attraction in the Northern Territory and is considered sacred space by Aborigines. The massive sandstone monolith is spectacular especially as its color varies through the day and appears scarlet by sunset. You can witness the awe-inspiring beauty of this site by clicking on *Sights and Sounds*.

Rock That Rocks
From a red rock to blues-rock. In Alice Springs, 325 kilometers (200 miles) northeast of Uluru National Park, the Central Australian Aboriginal Media Association has established a recording studio to preserve and foster traditional and contemporary aboriginal music. Click on *Australia: Aboriginal Rock of Central Australia* in *Sights and Sounds* for a sample.

Australia is home to many other musicians as well. It may be hard to imagine rock music as a commodity, but exports of Australian rock music exceeded $200 million (Australian) annually in the 1990s. Among the country's more internationally notable rockers are: AC/DC, Air Supply, Crowded House, INXS,

Little River Band, Men at Work, Midnight Oil, Savage Garden, Silverchair, and Rick Springfield. The Little River Band is the only one of these artists to have a geographical name. (The Little River, also known as the Boyd River, is located in New South Wales.) That is, unless you count Rick Springfield as a location. Springfield is a small coastal town in Queensland near the sugar-refining city of Bundaberg, a popular destination for snorkelers along the Great Barrier Reef. Check out the slide show by selecting *Sights and Sounds* and surf the reef with a variety of *Web links*!

The Rocks
If you are still looking for more examples of rocks in Australia, take a cybervisit to historic downtown Sydney and tour *The Rocks*, a restored colonial district and tourist attraction near the famous Sydney Opera House located near the famous Harbor Bridge. Explore the many *Web links* for Sydney and take a virtual tour of the city from the harbor and from space via the Sights and Sounds.

Keywords: Australia, Uluru Rock, Aboriginal Music, Great Barrier Reef, Sydney

Want to Know Samoa?
Read On!

If you have ever taken a geography test and were required to identify some of the islands sprinkled in the western Pacific you probably were learning these locations for the first time. After all, how often do you get to travel to such far-flung places as Samoa or Fiji? While these islands are often thought of as exotic vacation destinations, there are many interesting facets to their cultures and economies that deserve attention. A virtual tour of the region would be a good place to start.

Samoa

Samoa is among the least developed economies in the world and struggles each year to cope with a serious trade-deficit. Their economy is largely dependent on tourism as well as primary sector activities including timbering and agriculture. What Samoa lacks in economic development it makes up for with a rich cultural heritage. Take some time and investigate this fascinating country. Using the *Find* icon, create a map of Samoa. Click on the country's capital, Apia, and then select *Geography*. What two western powers fought for control of this region in the late 1800s? Are you surprised at the type of manufacturing taking place in such a remote location? You can take a tour of Samoa via *Sights and Sounds*. You can also experience a Samoan sasa dance by selecting Society and clicking on the *dance video image*. Read the section on *Recreation* and find out if you would like to have a giant helping of palolo for dinner tonight. Want Samoa?

Fiji
Can you name an international celebrity from Fiji? Ever hear of Vijay Singh, the professional golfer? He may very well be the most famous person from Fiji in contemporary culture. But even for a sports star, it's a long way from Fiji to Pebble Beach. What if you were a spectator at a golf tournament and had an opportunity to meet Mr. Singh? What would you say? Perhaps you might want to impress him with your knowledge of the Pacific region. To prepare yourself, use *Find* and bring up a map of *Fiji*. Learn about Fiji's culture and history by selecting *Society*. Take a closer look at the islands by choosing *Sights and Sounds*. And wouldn't Mr. Singh be impressed if you could greet him at the first tee in his native tongue? What? Fijian isn't a language requirement for your major? No problem. Go to *Web Links* and select *Common Fijian Words and Phrases*. Now, using this Fijian language Web page, translate the following hypothetical conversation.

Mr. Singh: Good morning
You: Ni sa yadra turaga.
Mr. Singh: You look like a brilliant geographer to me. Do you know anything about my native land of Fiji?
You: Vakalailai.
Mr. Singh: Could you locate my hometown of Lautoka on a map?
You: Io!

Mr. Singh: Pardon me but you are sitting on my clubs!

You: Tulou!

Mr. Singh: How many large islands comprise Fiji?

You: Rua.

Mr. Singh: How many rooms in a traditional Fijian "burus?"

You: Dua.

Mr. Singh: Why, you ARE a brilliant geographer!

You: Vinaka vakelevu!

For more information on Fijian language and culture, explore other *Web Links* including *Languages of Fiji--Ethnologue Database*, and *Welcome to the Fiji Islands*. Sa moce!

Keywords: Western Samoa, Culture, Fiji, Language, Pacific Ocean

Part Two

Activities for *Human Geography* Using Encarta® Virtual Globe

Rocky Mountain High (and Corn Belt Low)

Almost thirty years ago, Peter Gould, a geographer now at Pennsylvania State University, introduced the notion of Mental Maps into the geographic literature. Using a sophisticated mathematical procedure known as factor analysis, he was able to produce isoline maps of residential preferences of students attending different universities in the country including his own. Figure 1-9 in your textbook provides two examples--the upper map is the view from California (specifically University of California, Los Angeles) and the lower map is that of students at Pennsylvania State University. The question that Gould asked of these students allowed them to really "blue sky" their responses as if they didn't have a care in the world other than choosing the most desirable residential location possible. The method used by Gould to extract the communality in the responses of the students has been criticized, but the maps that are produced continue to fascinate.

Most students had a strong preference for their home state irrespective of the fact they were told they could disregard family obligations. Gould called this the local dome effect.

Secondly, there was a general national trend in evidence. In the late 1960s, students preferred California--it was usually selected second only to the home state. The residential desirability surface then followed the topography of the country in a manner of speaking. The Great Basin states (e.g., Nevada, Utah) were ranked as low as their relative elevations. The desirability surface then rose as the Rocky Mountains loomed to the east but fell again beyond the front range of the Rockies and remained low all across the agricultural Great Plains and Corn Belt states. The residential desirability surface then rose toward the Middle Atlantic States and those along the Eastern Seaboard until the Mason-Dixon Line was reached. For most students in the country in the 1960s, the South was the least desirable region. Students in the South, however, didn't see it that way at all. They had a highly differentiated view of the South. Students at the University of Alabama, for example, liked their home state (i.e., they displayed a local dome effect) but rather disliked Mississippi right next door.

Preferences do change over time. Perhaps because of the popularity of skiing and the songs by the late John Denver, Colorado has now replaced California as the most residentially desirable state outside of the home state for most college students. The South has changed dramatically. Peninsular Florida was always ranked higher than the remainder of the Southern states, but now states along the Atlantic seaboard (especially Virginia and North Carolina) and the state of Georgia have improved tremendously in their perceived residential desirability. These expressed preferences are being mirrored by patterns of net in-migration to these formerly despised states as well. The biggest losers are states in the agricultural Middle West. Iowa is now last in the residential preference of Pennsylvania students for example. Why do you think this is the case? We would like you to focus your attention on two of the most maligned states--Iowa and Ohio; two states that have slipped quite a bit in the residential preferences of students at The Pennsylvania State University at least.

In order to make a fair comparison, we would like you to focus your attention on comparable *Web Links*. Click *Find* and pick each state in turn. Under *Web Links* chose the official site for state tourism information and the *Rough Guide* which is available for both states. According to Iowa's *Official Iowa Division of Tourism* site what is their new motto for the state? Does it make you smile? Investigating further under *More Fun Facts*, can you tell us what is Iowa's only town located on an island? Did Abraham Lincoln own land in Iowa? Was Des Moines always the state capital? Where is the site of the largest Danish settlement in the United States? What does Cedar Rapids share in common only with Paris, France? And, finally, how many covered bridges are there in Madison County? Now click on the Web site for the *Rough Guide to Iowa* and then click again on *Into Region* which focuses on eastern Iowa. What has happened since 1991 to enliven that part of the state and make it more attractive to tourists? Who founded The Amana Colonies? Were they a communist society? What are they best known for today?

Now *Find* Ohio and click on the *Web Links* that will take you to *Ohio Tourism*. We can't visit everywhere in the state, so let's focus on one of the more maligned areas of the state--the area along the shoreline of Lake Erie. Cleveland has even been referred to in a derogatory way as the "Mistake by the Lake". Click in turn the information for tourist attractions number 1 (*Cedar Point*), 5 (*Rock and Roll Hall of Fame and Museum*) and 11 (*Lake Erie Islands*). Can you answer the following questions: What is nicknamed "America's Rollercoast?" Who designed the Rock and Roll Hall of Fame? What is its most prominent architectural feature? What whole island is on the National Register of Historic Places? Now click on the Web link for the *Rough Guide to Ohio*. Click again on *Into Region* that focuses on the Lake Erie shoreline area and nearby islands. What crop was grown on the islands in Lake Erie in the 1860s? What is being memorialized at the Glacial Grooves State Memorial?

Do you find Iowa and Ohio more attractive now?

Keywords: mental map, local dome effect, national trend, Iowa, Ohio

You Are My Density

It is clear from the material that you've read in the textbook that the distribution of population around the planet is uneven. There are huge areas of population void where very few people live. Alternatively there are rich and fertile areas where the population crams onto every available parcel of arable land (i.e., land capable of producing a crop). Over half of the world's population lives on the flat and fertile floodplains of major rivers especially in South, Southeast, and East Asia. These are sensitive, low-lying ecological zones subject to periodic flooding and other natural disasters. Eventually many may be at risk due to ocean level rise if global warming continues unabated.

Can you name a few of the major population-void areas? They include much of the polar region where the growing season (if there even is one) is too short to grow crops. There are large tracts of desert in northern and southwestern Africa, northern Chile, Mexico and the southwestern United States, the outback of Australia, central Asia, and elsewhere in which it is difficult to sustain life. Finally, there are tropical rainforest areas that despite the verdant look of the landscape are incapable of supporting large populations. Tropical soils are often of poor quality because they are deficient in organic matter (humus) and leached of important (but water-soluble) minerals.

What is the consequence of large areas of population void and concentration for the countries (i.e., states) of the world? Let's focus more closely on one of the countries listed in Table 6-1 (The Netherlands) and another that is not (Brazil). The table presents you with the difference between the arithmetic density (i.e., population divided by total land area) and the physiologic density (i.e., population divided by total arable land area). In some cases, there are huge differences between the two figures. For example, over 90 percent of Egypt's rapidly growing population lives within the floodplain of the Nile River or one of its tributaries. Most of the rest of the country is a sandy desert. The country of Egypt is very large and if we simply divide the population of Egypt (about 62 million people according to Table 6-1 in your text) by the size of the country, we obtain the figure that most people think of when they hear the word "density". It is more properly called arithmetic density. What is misleading about arithmetic density in the case of Egypt? What is Egypt's physiologic density? Among the countries shown in Table 6-1, Egypt displays the greatest disparity between arithmetic and physiologic density. What is another country in which the physiologic density might be many times higher than the arithmetic density?

The problem with Table 6-1 is that results are already calculated for you. That's the easy way! We want you to realize how the figures you see there were actually derived in a hands-on manner. We hope that by so doing you won't take for granted the statistics that you see in a table or even the definition of terminology, such as the term "arable." As defined in Resource D Glossary (p. R-27 in the text), arable literally means cultivable. "Land fit for cultivation by one farming method or another." Is land devoted to the pasturing of livestock considered arable? Why or why not? What about idle land brought into production but is not currently being used. Is it arable? The operative word in the definition of arable is "cultivatable." Explain a possible difference between cultivated and cultivable.

Let's start with a country, The Netherlands, for which densities have already been calculated. What is the amount of arable land in The Netherlands? We cannot tell directly from Table 6-1 but we can derive that figure indirectly. The physiologic density of the Netherlands is 4,425 persons per square mile, approximately 4.54 times greater than the arithmetic density of 974 persons per square mile. Thus, dividing the total land area by this 4.54 factor, will yield the approximate amount of land that is considered arable in The Netherlands--about 3.2 thousand square miles; almost 20 percent of the total land area. Let's see if we can verify the amount of arable land using Encarta's *Virtual Globe*. Click on *Find*. Then click on *Country* to find the Netherlands. Do a search of basic statistics to see if arable land is easily obtainable. Check *Facts and Figures* and then *Statistics* (especially for *Agriculture*). Interestingly, it is nowhere to be found.

Now click on *Web Links* and open to the address labeled *Key Figures and Statistics—The Netherlands*. One can certainly find a gold mine of information at this Web site. For example, click on *Agriculture, forestry and fisheries*. Once there, click on *Arable*

Crops. How many hectares of land are devoted to the cultivation of Triticale? Does The Netherlands have a problem with Tribbles? What is triticale? Allusions to old Star Trek episodes aside, it isn't easy to find the amount of arable land; even if we did the amount might be expressed in terms of hectares (about 2.2 acres) rather than square miles or square kilometers.

Is it any easier to determine the amount of arable land for a country not listed in Table 6-1? Without a consistent data source such as the United Nations Food and Agriculture Yearbook, it isn't easy to compare statistics for different countries. Click on *Find Country* and then *Brazil*. Study the map of Brazil carefully. There are few large cities in the states of Rondonia, Amazonas, and Mato Grosso except for Manaus. Even Manaus was a much more important center in the past than it is now. Why are these three states seemingly so sparsely populated? Click onto the *Web Links* and go to the source called *Brazil Quick Facts*. Note that the percentage of arable land in Brazil is estimated to be seven percent of the total. Using that percentage, calculate the arithmetic and physiologic densities of the country. Hint: click on *Facts and Figures* and you will find that Brazil is 3,286,490 square miles in size, only slightly smaller than the United States and that there were 161,790,000 people living there in 1995. Calculate the two densities. If you need to provide a check on your calculation of arithmetic density, refer to *Facts and Figures* for the Netherlands.

Keywords: Brazil, Netherlands, arithmetic density, physiological density

Like Salmon Swimming Upstream?

From at least the time of Ernst Ravenstein over a century ago, the metaphor of migration waves forming streams of migrants has been used to describe a restless world population on the move. Ravenstein is credited as the first social scientist who studied human migration in a systematic and conceptual way. One of his "laws" of human migration sounds a little like Newton's second law of thermodynamics--for every stream of migration there will eventually be a counterstream. Is this true even for the "flood" of African-Americans leaving the rural South after the turn of this century in search a better life in the Northeast, Middle West, and West?

The answer is decidedly yes. In fact, since about 1970, the "Great Migration", as it is often called, has reversed itself. In the 1980 census period, the percentage of African-Americans living in the South began to increase, the first time that had happened since before the turn of the century. And, the 1980 census figures were no flukes. The 1990 census continues to bear out the fact that there is now a counterstream of African-Americans moving to the South. In some cases, they are moving back to the South they had left behind decades before. In other cases, northern urban African-Americans are moving to the South for the first time. These latter African-Americans, with no particular close family ties to the South, are overwhelmingly moving to the cities of the South whereas African-Americans with family ties to certain parts of the South were often moving back "home", even to some very rural and poverty-stricken areas.

What is the impact of the Great Migration on the spatial distribution of African-American population in the United States? The statistics reveal a tremendous impact. In 1900, at the start of the Great Migration, 90 percent of all African-Americans lived in the South and the vast majority of them in the rural South where they were, for the most part, sharecroppers and agricultural workers. By 1970, at the end of the Great Migration, only 50 percent of the African-American population remained in the South and even in this home (i.e., origin) region, many African-Americans had moved to the towns and cities of the region rather than remaining on the land in rural areas. Examine Figure 11-7 (p. 128) in the textbook closely. The darkish red areas delimit counties that contain the highest relative proportion of African-Americans. How would you describe the geographic distribution displayed here? In what ways is such a map misleading? Even if only 20 percent of New York City's population is African-American, the absolute number of African-Americans would still be several hundred fold greater than the 80-90 percent figure found in many Southern counties.

Many of the counties with the highest relative percentages of African-Americans are rural counties on the Carolina-Georgia Piedmont, the "Black Belt" crescent-shaped region of rich black marl soils straddling Alabama and Mississippi and the lower

Mississippi River valley from west Tennessee into northern Louisiana. What do these areas have in common? If a map of cotton production for the early 1900s were shown, the two patterns would look remarkably similar.

Why did African-Americans leave this Southern region in such large numbers after the turn of the century? As with any migration movement that is voluntary, there are myriad causes. One, the economic structure of the region was changing. Agriculture was becoming more mechanized and the need for unskilled labor to sow, cultivate, and harvest the crops was diminishing. The mood of the South at the time was one of racial intolerance with public facilities that were separate but very seldom equal. There were Jim Crow laws on the books specifying where and when African-Americans could gather and where they could not. There was the ever present threat of mob lynching of African-Americans and an "invisible empire" of Ku Klux Klans and organizations of their ilk intent on preserving the white man's privilege (i.e., the status quo) at all cost. Demographers, scientists who study population issues, would call all the above factors push factors. There were also pull factors luring rural African-Americans to the high-paying factory jobs of the Northeast, Middle West (i.e., North Central), and West regions of the country. The migration streams were boosted during WWI when the need for factory workers became critical and African-Americans provided the necessary labor. That demand continued during the rapidly expanding "roaring '20s" and then bottomed out during the Great Depression of the 1930s only to come roaring back with the war effort during WWII and the post-war boom economy of the 1950s and early 1960s.

The streams of migration are quite predictable and rational. African-Americans that initially resided along the Atlantic coastal plain migrated to cities in the Northeast and most ended up in the southernmost cities in that region (e.g., Washington, D.C. and Baltimore) than their more northerly counterparts (e.g., Boston and New York). Likewise, African-Americans from states in the East South Central region such as Mississippi were more likely to go to industrial centers of the Middle West such as Chicago and Detroit. Those originally in the West South Central region such as Texas were more likely to migrate to the Far West region, especially Los Angeles and the San Francisco Bay area.

Not surprisingly, the counterstreams of African-Americans moving to the South reflect the same pattern in reverse. It's much more likely for a retired African-American factory worker from Chicago to migrate to the Yazoo Delta of Mississippi than to southern Georgia or the North Carolina coastal plain.

Let's examine one city that was heavily influenced by the influx of African-Americans during the Great Migration. Click on *Find Countries* and type in *United States*. Then click on *Sights and Sounds* and note the caption and the sound clip for Chicago. What type of music is featured in many popular Chicago nightclubs? Koko Taylor is a blues artist of rare talent but many of the other people mentioned including Muddy Waters sing a form of music known as the Delta blues. What distinguishes this type of music from other genres? Where is the Delta?

How did so many African-Americans end up in Chicago after the turn of the century and especially after WW I? Let's examine a Web Site that is not reached by Encarta, but rather by one of several search engines that you might have access to (e.g., Yahoo, Lycos). One of the best sites available is: HYPERLINK http://lcweb.loc.gov/exhibits/african/afamo11.html You will be linked to a Library of Congress Web site location entitled "Chicago: Destination for the Great Migration: African-American Mosaic Exhibition" which is part of their collection "The African-American Mosaic: A Library of Congress Resource Book for the Study of Black History and Culture." What Chicago newspaper was especially influential in attracting African-Americans to the city? What was the African-American community that grew up on Chicago's South side in a era of Jim Crow laws and housing discrimination called? Was there any geographical sorting of the African-American population noticeable within this community? What was the basis of that sorting? Where did the more elite African-Americans live within Chicago?

Keywords: migration stream, counterstream, push factors, pull factors, African-Americans, Great Migration, Chicago

Not So Great (Life) Expectations

Why is it that the average life expectancy (averaging both sexes together) is greater than 80 years in the tiny principality of San Marino, an enclave within Italy and less than 40 years in the west African country of Sierra Leone? What are the determinants of life expectancy?

There is no simple answer to that question but we can do some investigating on our own using the Statistics portion of Encarta's Virtual Globe. First click on *Options* and then on *World Statistics*. The amount of information can be overwhelming. While not every demographic statistic is listed here, five variables listed under the Health and Education section will suffice for our purposes. The variable that we wish to explain (referred to as the dependent variable in statistics) is Life Expectancy at Birth (1995). For now, we will not concern ourselves with possible gender differences such as differential access to proper nutritional and health care facilities. Using the *Statistical Tables* option, display these national level data in an array from high to low. Choose the countries in the world with life expectancies greater than or equal to 78 years. List these countries in the array. How would you characterize the location of these countries if you had to generalize about them? Now list the bottom of the array--the countries in the world with average life expectancies less than or equal to 46 years. How would you characterize their pattern? The greatest life expectancies (with a few exceptions) are found in the countries of Western Europe and the lowest life expectancies are almost all found in African nations.

Let's examine some variables that might be related to life expectancy that we might posit as explanatory or independent variables. There are five in the Health and Education group that should be related to our dependent variable-total life expectancy. These include: access to pure water in rural areas, access to pure water in the country as a whole, the average caloric intake of the populations residing in various countries, the number of people for every available hospital bed, and the infant morality rate.

Let's hypothesize what we'd expect to find when comparing each independent variable separately with our dependent variable-life expectancy. One of the things that many of us in the United States take for granted is access to pure drinking water but such is not the case in many parts of the Third World. Contaminated water can cause all sorts of problems from the spread of deadly diseases like cholera to the more mundane but equally deadly diarrheal diseases like dysentery. Such water-borne diseases kill many young infants and as such, safe water and infant morality rates are undoubtedly interrelated.

Access to pure water is sometimes easier to obtain in the city where there are water purification plants than in the rural countryside where the water might be drawn more directly from contaminated rivers or wells.

The number of people per available hospital bed would be a measure of the quality of the health care delivery system. Advanced economies should have lower numbers than their Third World counterparts.

The caloric supply daily (per capita) may be a bit more complicated. To avoid malnutrition and other complications that can lead to premature death, people should consume a certain minimum number of calories to maintain body weight and aid in cell repair. But, there can also be too much of a good thing leading to an overweight and out-of-shape population. At the beginning of the century it was generally held that the average person needed to consume 3,500 calories per day. Now we know that it's healthier to consume about 2,000 calories a day.

Finally, a large contributor to a relatively short life expectancy is the infant mortality rate. That is, the number of children born alive who do not make it through the first year of life. Lack of health care facilities or a pure water supply will increase the infant mortality rate.

Using the *Table of Statistics* option, compare the arrayed data for access to safe water (total) with that for the dependent variable. Are there any overlaps (i.e., countries that appear on both lists)? Six of the twelve countries at the high end of the life expectancy table also have the highest value population with access to pure water (100 percent). Alternatively, four of the 10 countries at the low end of the water accessibility scale (33 percent or less of the population possessing such access) are among the countries with the lowest life expectancies. The results are similar if we consider just access of rural areas to pure water supplies. Six of the countries in which 100 percent of the rural population has access to pure water are also those countries with the highest life expectancy. Three of the 10 countries with the worst rural access to safe water (less than 17 percent) have the lowest life expectancies.

Why are there fewer matches between dependent and independent variables in the case of the number of persons per hospital bed? Two of the countries with the lowest life expectancies also had the highest number of persons per available hospital bed. Which countries are they? At the other end of the array showing the countries with the best access to hospitals as measured by the number of persons per available hospital bed there was only one match. One might conclude that this surrogate (i.e., easily measured substitute) of access to health care delivery is not the best. What is unusual about the countries that have the best access to hospital facilities? All but one is an independent state that emerged from the breakup of the Soviet Union. They have hospitals, but are those facilities equipped with the latest technologies and medicines? That is highly doubtful.

The best match is the relationship between infant mortality rate and life expectancy. Eight of the 10 countries in the world with the highest infant mortality rates (mainly confined to the continent of Africa) are also those with the lowest life expectancy. Likewise, six of the 12 countries with the lowest infant mortality rates (less that eight infants dying for every 1,000 born alive) also have the highest life expectancies. Which countries are they? Why, in your opinion, isn't the United States among those countries of the world with the lowest infant mortality rates?

Keywords: infant mortality rate, life expectancy, access to health care and sanitation, dependent variable, independent variable

A Woman's Place is in the House...and in the Senate

This title appears on many car bumpers and it turns an old cliché on its head. Women are working outside the home in record numbers now and, as they assume greater positions of responsibility, the disparity in wages between what men and women are paid comparable jobs is closing. A disparity is still present, though, and many women feel they are called upon to balance work and home life to a much greater extent than their male counterparts. Likewise, professional women often complain of a glass ceiling, an invisible but nonetheless very real barrier to their progress through the professional ranks of major businesses simply because of their gender.

These are serious disparities to deal with in our modern society. There are even greater disparities between men and women in other parts of the world. At worst, women are treated like chattel, as objects of value incapable of making their own decisions outside the confines of the home of the girl's father or woman's husband. In some patriarchal societies women are denied access to the most basic of opportunities based solely on their gender.

Let's examine two statistics that might indicate the lower status of women in many traditionally based societies--female literacy and the fertility rate. Click on *Find* and go to *Statistics*. Under *Health and Education* is the statistic Literacy Rate, Female 1995.

Interestingly, almost half of the countries in the world, including the United States, do not provide these data. Examine the data in tabular form arrayed in order of the percentage of females that are literate. What can be said about the countries at the bottom? Where are they located?

Now, examine the same statistic for males (i.e., Literacy rate, male 1995). Again, array the data in descending order of percentage of the male population that is literate. Is there a strong positive association between countries where females are mostly illiterate and those where males are also found in the same basic condition? The answer is decidedly yes, but even in these countries, males typically have a higher literacy rate. What is the approximate factor (i.e., multiple) that would make male and female literacy in these countries approximately equal?

Another sobering statistic is the fertility rate. It is defined as the number of children that the average woman gives birth to during her childbearing years (usually defined as age 15-45). Click on *Statistics* and then *Population* to find this statistic. Take a minute to comprehend that in the countries at the top of the array, located mostly in northern and sub-Saharan Africa, the average woman gives birth to seven or more children during her child-bearing years! Is it little wonder that women in these countries seldom work outside the home?
Let's go beyond the statistics. Click on *Find* and then *Content*. Type in *women* as the subject. An overwhelming number of sites come up, but pay attention to those that first appear on the screen without moving the side bar. To explore the subject

of women in various societies further, you might like to examine the other sites on your own.

Focus on Saudi Arabia and the role of women in that society and then answer the following questions: How many wives can a Saudi man have under Islamic law? Does he need to seek the permission of his other wives before he can take another? What is the veil called that women in Saudi Arabia wear that covers their face? Can a woman ride a bicycle in public? Can an unmarried man and woman go on a date alone in Saudi Arabia? What do they call the money that a man may have to pay the family of a bride in order to marry her? Can a woman doctor in Saudi Arabia examine a man? Under what conditions is that possible?

Religion may have an effect on the birth and fertility rates. The Roman Catholic Church, for example, forbids the use of artificial means of contraception among its adherents. This conservative view was recently reinforced in *Veritas Splendor*, an encyclical (religious statement) issued by Pope John Paul II. Why do the nominally Catholic countries of Italy and Spain have among the lowest fertility rates in the world? Does it have something to do with the percentage of women in the labor force (i.e., working outside the home)?

Keywords: Literacy Rate, Fertility Rate, Women's Issues, Gender

What'll it Be: Lethargic and Clever or Vigorous and Stupid?

One of the unfortunate legacies of early theorizing in geography derives from a school of thought known as environmental determinism. That school goes back to the ancient Greeks who first coined the word "geography" to define their scientific attempt to describe and understand the known world of their time. Interestingly, one of the contributors to this body of Greek literature about geography was Hippocrates, the great physician. Doctors to this day still pledge allegiance to the Hippocratic oath. They promise to "first, do no harm". Hippocrates wrote *On Airs, Waters and Places*, an early geographic compendium in the 5th century BCE. In it, he tried to explain the progress of human civilizations around the known world of the time--portions of Europe, Asia, and Africa. He noted that within the frigid climate of the northern European plain were roving bands of kinship-based societies that we know today as Huns, Visigoths, and Ostragoths. These tribes were not as advanced as the Greeks in many of the finer aspects of civilized culture (e.g., theatre, the arts, athletic competition, scholarly pursuits). These tribes were a strong, militaristic lot. It was as if, being too far from the sun's warming rays, these people lacked intelligence but made up for it with their physical prowess.

Likewise, to the south of Greece in the torrid zone closer to the equator lived groups of people who were

64

very intelligent and clever, having sailed their dhows around the Red Sea and beyond to uncover the riches of sub-Saharan Africa. But these people were judged to be living too close to the sun and were, therefore, lethargic. They had to take a break during the heat of the day, for example, as if the sun had sapped them of their energy.

In between, was the temperate (actually Mediterranean) climate of the Greek peninsula that, like Goldilocks inspecting Baby Bear's things, was found to be just right. Not too hot. Not too cold. Just the right combination of vigor and intelligence. In other words, Hippocrates was not only ethnocentric but he explained the differences in the degree of sophistication of the world's known civilizations by their location relative to aspects of the physical environment--in this case--climate. That is, the physical environment was held to determine people's behavior. In a nutshell that's what environmental determinism is all about.

Your textbook presents a more modern day application of the same theoretical stance--Ellsworth Huntington's view of climate and civilization (see Figure 19-1 on p. 230). Writing in the early part of this century, Huntington, a geography professor at Yale, was very influential. His most famous theory may have been the beating heart of Asia in which he argued that the "ruthless, ideal-less horsemen" that we call the Tartars or Mongols have influenced the histories of both China and Russia. Like a beating heart, when the climate cycle was in a period of adequate rainfall, the range of the nomadic Mongols and their herds of horses, camels, yaks, and other livestock, contracted to central Asia and present-day Mongolia. But, when the climate went into an extended period of drought, the range of forage, of necessity, had to expand. The ancient Russians eventually had to move their capital from Kiev, in the grassland prairie, to Moscow, in the forested zone, so that they could better defend themselves against these mounted invaders. What two physical features did the mounted horsemen from Mongolia encounter as they rode toward Kiev (the present day capital of Ukraine)? Click on *Find* and then *Russia* and choose the *Physical Features* type of map. Now switch to the *Climate* map of the same area. In what climatic regime do we find Kiev? Moscow?

How did the economy of China differ from that in Mongolia at the time when Huntington argued his theory was appropriate? The Chinese were, for the most part, farmers and not nomadic herdsmen. The richest farmland was along the floodplains of the two major rivers that run through China. What are the names of those rivers? Click on *China* and then choose the *Physical Features* type of map. Where is the mouth of each of these major rivers? What did the Chinese do to keep the Mongols out of their agricultural villages located along the floodplains of the Yangtze (i.e., Chang Jiang) and Huang He Rivers? Click on *Find* and then *Content* and type in "Great Wall of China". When was this most massive of man-made features begun? When was it completed? The Great Wall of China is one of the few man-made features that can be seen by the astronauts from space.

Geography suffered a "burnt fingers" reaction to environmental determinism. We dabbled in theory and were eventually excoriated for it. Many geographers unfortunately clung tenaciously to this model long after it was rejected and repudiated in most other disciplines. This way of thinking--that there is a one-way causative relationship between the physical environment and human behavior--is too simplistic. Some geographers overreacted however and denied that the physical environment had any effect on human behavior. Behavior, it was thought by these geographers, is constrained only by the human mind itself. Do you think that this more humanistic way of viewing the nature of human-environment relationships is an example of "throwing out the baby with the bath water?" Why or why not?

Keywords: Environmental Determinism, Ellsworth Huntington, "beating heart of Asia", Hippocrates

You Are What You Speak: African Lingua Francae

The intricate mosaic of African languages reveals much of the continent's complex blend of indigenous and colonial history and culture. No less than seven language families are represented ranging from Indo-European in South Africa, Malay-Polynesian in Madagascar, to Afro-Asiatic in the Saharan north. Along the border between the Afro-Asiatic languages of the north and the Niger-Congo languages of sub-Saharan Africa, lies a transition zone where two major lingua francae, Swahili and Hausa, dominate. Swahili evolved from Bantu, Arabic, and Persian languages while Hausa is a blend of Sudanic and Afro-Asiatic tongues. Lingua franca literally means "Frankish language" as explained in the glossary of your textbook (p. R-32). It was a mixture of languages that could be more generally understood within a wider geographic region than was the case with any of the composite languages considered separately. But, language is more than words and phrases. Our language literally shapes our world view (cosmology). Our words are our world as an anthropologist of language once put it. Language can tell a story within a story. It can also be a song and Africa is a wonderful place to listen.

Travel to Somalia and listen to an "Urban Love Song" in *Sights and Sounds*. How does the history of the "Coastal Town of Baraawe" relate to the evolution of traditional Somalian music? Now, compare this with the Swahili lyrics of a Tanzanian song. Go to Tanzania and click on *Sights and Sounds*. Select "Tanzania: Urban Dance Music" and listen to the dance-style music. The Cuban influence on Tanzanian popular music can be experienced by going to Cuba and selecting "Popular Dance Music" in *Sights and Sounds*. In what ways does this music sound similar or different?

Hausa is the lingua franca for millions of people living in a cluster of countries in west Africa. Hausa is the language of commerce in Niger and the language spoken on "Radio Niger." Create a of *map of Niger* and read about *Language in Society*. What is the official language of Niger and why is it only spoken by a minority of country's residents? You can visit a typical village in Niger by clicking on Sights and Sounds and selecting "Life in a Hausa Village." How has migration and mobility influenced language? Listen to a "Hausa Praise Song." How does this compare to the Swahili-influenced music of eastern Africa? Another example of Hausa can be heard by moving south on your map to Nigeria. Click on *Sights and Sounds* and listen to the sample of Nigerian "Hausa Music." In what ways is this music similar or different than the Hausa music of Niger? Now go to *Web Links* and select "Languages of Nigeria--Ethnologue Database." How many languages are spoken in Nigeria? How does this necessitate the need for a lingua franca?

African countries are not alone in the use of lingua francae. Use the *Find Content* tool and search for the words "lingua franca" and go to that location. Why did a lingua franca emerge in this place? How is it different or similar in its origins from Swahili or Hausa?

Keywords: language, Swahili, Hausa, Africa, lingua franca

Christianity Worldwide: Plain Vanilla or 31 Flavors?

As you have gathered by now, this activity guide sometimes dwells on aspects that the textbook authors choose not to and vice versa. Together, the book and this companion volume often complement each other. It is common for introductory cultural textbooks to focus on the exotic and the faraway, especially when it comes to the subject of religion. For example, not many of us know a great deal about the state religion of Japan, Shinto. Textbooks will often dwell on topics such as: 1) the differences among the Eastern religions; 2) interesting cultural practices such as the avoidance of certain foods and drink within the belief systems of different religions; 3) the diffusion of the main branches of Islam from their core area in southwestern Asia.

Your textbook authors note that there are three truly universal (and universalizing) religions in the world: Islam, certain forms of Buddhism, and Christianity. The one that usually gets short shrift is Christianity probably because it is too close to home, too familiar, and seemingly too well known. But is Christianity really practiced similarly throughout the world or it is reflective of the local indigenous culture in which it is found? Let's see what we can find out. The United States presents an interesting mosaic of practice in an ostensibly secular but majority Christian country. Take a look at the map of dominant religions in the United States (Figure 25-2 p. 315). Whether it is the

71

Mormon in Utah or the French Catholic in Louisiana, all fall into the general category of Christian. And although the Jewish population of the greater New York metropolitan area supposedly exceeds that of Israel, Judaism is still not so dominant that it could be detected on a map of this scale. The regional distribution of religion in the United States is often reflective of the origins of the earliest settlers in the region. For example, where did most of the settlers of the upper Midwest (e.g., Minnesota, the Dakotas) come from originally? What religion is the state church in those countries (if any)? Let's now look at a few countries in Europe. What about the birthplace of the Protestant Reformation--Germany? Click on the *Find* command and then *Countries*. When you have Germany specified, click on *Society* on the sidebar. Choose *Religion*. Where are most of the Lutherans in Germany located? What about the Roman Catholics—where are they located? The article mentions a growing Muslim presence in Germany. What might be the source of Islamic immigration into Germany or do you think this increase represents instead a conversion of an increasing proportion of this large secular society to the tenants of the Islamic faith? Let's examine three more countries in Europe: Belgium, with two distinct culture subregions; Poland, homeland of the current Pope of the Roman Catholic Church; and Bulgaria, a former Warsaw-pact nation in Eastern Europe. Bulgaria was formerly part of the Islamic Ottoman Empire, but a country that, like Poland, also endorsed the official state atheism of a Communist regime until very recently. Click onto the *Society* sidebar and then choose the *Religion* category for each of the three European countries in turn.

If there is such a linguistic and cultural division between Flemish northern Belgium and the Walloon population of southern Belgium, why is a large percentage of the population in both parts Roman Catholic? The write-up suggests that Flemish residents are more religious than the Walloons. If the Flemish area in the north has a closer affinity to the Dutch and the Walloons in the south have a close affinity to the French, why is Catholicism seemingly stronger in the northern part of the country, adjacent as it is to the influence of the Reformed Church (Protestant) in the Netherlands?

Poland is a very Roman Catholic country. When did this conversion to Catholicism take place? What town in Poland is Pope John Paul II from originally? What role did the Roman Catholic Church play in the opposition to Communism? In your own words what does it mean to coexist but not cooperate with the Communists? What is unusual about the Uniate faith to which a minority of the Polish population adheres?

Why are Bulgarians members of the Bulgarian Orthodox Church rather than being adherents of Roman Catholicism? Briefly describe The Great Schism and the division between the Roman and Byzantine Empires. Click on the photograph of the *Alexander Nevsky Chapel* and read the caption. Where is the chapel? What does the construction of the chapel symbolize? Why does Bulgaria feel indebted to Russia?

Keywords: Roman Catholic Church, Protestantism, Orthodox Church, Belgium, Poland, Bulgaria

Let Them Eat Jute: The Colonial Legacy in World Agriculture

In most Third World countries, it is all the farmers can do to keep up with the internal demands of their country for foodstuffs. Little surplus is produced for export. In fact, many of these countries have to import foodstuffs despite the high proportion of the labor force engaged in agriculture. The text discusses the Third or Green Revolution in which high yielding varieties of grain have helped to stave off world hunger by increasing the world's food supply at least temporarily.

Long before the Third Revolution began, valuable arable land that could have been devoted to food crops was being taken out of production. Some of this land, especially in the tropics, was devoted to the growth of crops that could not be grown in Europe (e.g., tea, coffee, tobacco, bananas) but had a growing demand. Much of this land was organized into plantations in which scientific principles of horticulture were applied on a large, commercial scale. By buying necessary inputs in bulk and marketing their products to a mass market, these plantations often achieved economies of scale compared to the small plot cultivators they might have been competing against.

In addition to feeding the culinary desires of their colonial overseers, commercial crops were also grown that could not be eaten. These included indigo, cotton, jute, sisal, and rubber. Many of these fiber and industrial crops could only be grown in tropical or subtropical poor countries located throughout Asia, Africa, and South America.

Let's look at two such industrial crops--cotton and jute. Everyone knows what cotton is, but what is jute and what is it used for? Click on *Find* and then *Content* and type in the word *jute*. Click on the slide *Sorting Jute for Export in Bangladesh*. You'll see jute is a cane-like plant with strong, stringy fibers that can be turned into cordage and sacking material. What we call "gunny sacks" are made from jute. Often the backing of tufted carpets is made of jute. It's a very tough natural fiber. What has been the effect of synthetic substitutes on the market for jute in the extremely poor country of Bangladesh? Click on the *IJO (International Jute Organization)*. Major growers of jute are trying to form a cartel-like arrangement with the major purchasers of the fiber. What are five countries are exporters of the product? How would you characterize the 21 countries that have signed the agreement as importers?

Click on *Find*, then *Statistics* and then *Agriculture*. One of the variables mapped at the world scale (and in tabular form) is cotton production. Countries with large populations grow cotton (e.g., India, China, Pakistan, United States) but cotton is relatively more important to some smaller countries as it represents a major source of export income. Let's focus on some of these countries through *Sights and Sounds*. Click on *Find*, and then *Content* and type in *cotton*. Many of the entries on the screen (without moving the sidebar down) are pictures of cotton production in some of these countries. Click on the slide *Cotton Harvesters near Samarqand in Uzbekistan*. The caption says cotton is the country's leading source of export income, but it has come into production at a terrible cost. What are some of the ecological and social problems caused by the commercial production of cotton in that country? Now look at *Sewing Egyptian Cotton*. What makes Egypt's cotton so special? Why do you think that long staple cotton (i.e., long fibers) is so in demand for clothing and textiles relative to its shorter staple counterpart? Now click on *Valuable Cotton Crop for Azerbaijan*. The caption focuses on changes in cotton production that have taken place since the fall of the Soviet regime. Why haven't state farm collectives been done away with completely? Now click on the slide of *Transporting Cotton in Burundi*. Compare and contrast the method of transporting cotton in this central African nation with that used by Azeri farmers in the previous slide. Which method is more likely to accrue economies of scale? Finally, click on *Tajik Cotton (19U*. Tajikistan is another of the former Soviet republics in central Asia. Why is irrigation of cotton there so disastrous? Click on a map of this central Asian region showing the independent states of Kazakhstan, Uzbekistan, and Tajikistan. What body of water might form the most important source of irrigation for cotton crops in these newly independent countries? This body of water has shrunk to about half of its former size in the last forty years--an ecological disaster of the worst kind for all of the surrounding states.

Keywords: Cotton, Jute, Bangladesh, Egypt, Uzbekistan, Azerbaijan, Tajikistan

Planet of the Apes?
The Primate City Distribution

Excuse the play on words. The term "Primate" in the chapter title has nothing to do with the apes you might find in the primate house of your local zoo. Rather, the term is related to the concept of primacy or dominance. Urban geographers have been curious about the role of cities as the engines of state economies since at least the time of Mark Jefferson, the geographer who, in the early part of this century, first coined the term "primate city distribution." What is a primate city distribution exactly and what is the alternative? According to a recent textbook, a primate city is defined as "an urban center more than twice the size of the next largest city in the country; has a high proportion of its nation's economic activity; most obvious in the less developed world." (Fisher, ed. 1992, p. 703).

The alternative to the primate city distribution is called the rank-size regularity or rank-size rule. If the cities in a country conform to the rank-size regularity, one can easily estimate the population of a city of any given rank simply by dividing the population of the largest city by the rank of the city in question. For example, the fourth ranked city should be one-fourth the population of the largest center and so on. When graphed on double logarithmic paper (i.e., the logarithm of rank is displayed on the X-axis and the logarithm of city population on the Y-axis), a straight-line relationship between city population and city rank is found.

These empirical generalizations about the relative size of cities within countries continue to fascinate geographers despite the fact that neither the primate city distribution nor the rank-size rule says anything about where the cities are located within the country or relative to each other.

The geographer who has gotten the most mileage out of these regularities is Brian J.L. Berry. More than thirty years ago, he explained the rank-size rule as the equivalent of a system at equilibrium. Granted, it is dynamic equilibrium. Some cities can grow meteorically, others can almost collapse but there is enough systemic order to maintain the rank size regularity despite the self-canceling effects of rise and fall just noted. In every decennial census period from 1790 to the present, the United States urban system has manifested an approximate rank-size regularity.

A bit more controversial is the notion that primacy implies underdevelopment and rank-size distributions are symptomatic of developed economies. Berry studied 38 different countries in the world and his results were mixed. Nonetheless, he concluded that countries with the following characteristics would be more likely to conform to a rank-size regularity: 1) long history of urbanization (hence China might be rank-size even though not well developed economically when Berry was writing); 2) large size (hence Brazil with its federal system and need for regional centers to effectively integrate the country might be rank # sized); 3) complex and multi-sectoral economy (hence the Czech Republic with its diversified, manufacturing economy might be more likely to be rank-sized than, say, Albania with its much simpler agriculturally-based economy; and 4) no recent history of colonization (hence the United States which has been independent since 1776 would be more likely to be rank-sized than say, Ghana, which gained its independence in the 1960s and for which Accra, the capital and major port, was the nexus of most colonial investment). Others argue that the relationship between city size distribution and level of economic development is murky at best.

We want you to decide if you think there is anything to the notion of primacy being associated with underdevelopment. Click on *Find* and then *Countries* and record three variables for each of the countries in a list that will follow. Click on the *Facts* and *Figures* sidebar for each country in turn. Under *Basic Facts* find the population of the largest city and the population of the second largest city. Under *Economy*, find the per capita gross domestic product (GDP) if it is available. Do this for the following ten countries: Botswana, Brazil, Canada, China, Czech Republic, France, Germany, United Kingdom, United States, and Vietnam. Five of these countries are considered developed and five are categorized as developing or emerging. Do the five developed countries all manifest a rank-size regularity? To answer this, calculate the ratio between the first and second largest city in the country (ignoring for a moment that the figures may have been recorded at different times). If that ratio is greater than 2.0, the country is said to have a primate distribution. How many of the five developed countries display primate distributions? How many of the five emerging nations do? How would you describe the correlation (association) between this measure of primacy and per capita GDP? Do you think that Berry was justified in his characterization of the rank-size regularity as a measure of development? Why or why not? Even the United States displays a value indicating the primacy of New York City. Will Los Angeles close the gap? Why or why not?

Keywords: primate city, rank-size rule, dynamic equilibrium, primacy

Maquiladora? Is That the Latest Latin Dance Craze?

No, maquiladora is not the latest dance craze that will finally replace the macarena. It is instead a newly-created Spanish word based on the concept of the maquila, a tax paid on flour for the privilege of having the grain ground into flour at a mill. The tax was equivalent to the value added by the manufacture of the grain into a more useful and valuable product. The concept has been broadened to include all kinds of manufactured goods. It usually refers to the practice of locating twin plants, one on each side of the international boundary between the United States and Mexico. These plants are able to seize upon those factors of production in which each country has a comparative advantage. In the case of Mexico, it would be a labor advantage especially if workers are paid in Mexican pesos. In the case of the United States, it would be capital availability, the distribution network, and the transportation system to deliver the products to their customers.

Let's focus on one area that has been greatly affected by the maquiladora concept--the urban conglomeration of San Diego, Calif. and Tijuana, Mexico. Indeed, these two communities on the international border are more functionally integrated than they ever have been in the past. Click on *Find* and then on *Places* and type *Tijuana*. Then go to the *Web Links* on the sidebar. When the *Web Links* are

81

listed, click on the one called *Border Project*. Then click on *The Factory*. Within this website there is both important text and a series of 15 slides with informative captions. After reading the material about "The Factory" and examining the accompanying slide set, answer the following questions. How many persons were employed in Tijuana maquiladoras in 1995? What rank do these maquiladora plants have as a generator of income for the Mexican economy? Of the approximate 2,300 maquiladora plants in Mexico, how many are located in Tijuana? When did the Mexican government build the Nueva Tijuana industrial park? Why was it built? What is Mesa de Otay? What percentage of the maquiladoras is linked to southern California according to a 1986 survey?

What provision in the North American Free Trade Agreement (NAFTA) has aided the NAFTA nations (i.e., Canada, the United States, and Mexico) when non-North American countries wish to locate maquiladora plants of their own? What Korean companies have recently built facilities in Tijuana as a result of the NAFTA? What sector of Japanese manufacturing has built or plans to build assembly plants on the border? What are they building on the San Diego side of the international border?

How many tractor-trailer trucks does Sony have going back and forth across the international boundary of the United States and Mexico on a daily basis? How many Americans cross the international boundary to go to work everyday in Tijuana according to a 1994 survey? How much do Mexican visitors spend on shopping goods in San Diego and its American suburbs each year? Why is Otay Mesa on the San Diego side of the border finally beginning to develop?

According to the slide captions, what does the sign of a man, woman, and child running mean? Where are these signs posted (Slide 10)? What, according to the caption accompanying Slide 11, might be erroneous about the sign? According to the caption that accompanies Slide 14, who are the main customers for the Factory Outlet Mall in San Ysidro, CA?

One of the biggest downsides to maquiladora plant locations is their impact on the environment, especially the pollution of the already near-toxic Tijuana River and the groundwater supplies. Click on the web site entitled *Tijuana River Pollution and Maquiladoras* for further information about this nagging problem of environmental enforcement especially on the Mexican side of the international boundary.

Keywords: Maquiladora, Tijuana, San Diego, NAFTA

The Yacht Sea People: Roll the Dice and End Up in Vancouver

There is a joke in British Columbia, Canada that Vancouver should be renamed Hongcouver or Vankong because of the large influx of former residents of Hong Kong into this thriving metropolitan area and Pacific Rim seaport. In fact, Vancouver has become the fastest growing metropolitan area in North America largely as a result of the recent Diaspora of former residents of Hong Kong, fleeing the country before it reverted to China in July 1997. Many of these Hong Kong residents are very wealthy and feared expropriation of their wealth by the Chinese government despite assurances that it would not happen.

Where have these Chinese people from Hong Kong moved to within the city of Vancouver? One guess would be in their traditional neighborhood often referred to as Chinatown. Despite the official change of name to the International District, locals still refer to the area as Chinatown with its distinctive red street lanterns and red telephone booths. Red is a color that brings good luck in Chinese cosmology. How large is the Chinatown of Vancouver? Click on *Find* and then *Places* and type in *Vancouver*. Then click on the *Sights and Sounds* sidebar and examine the caption in the slide of Chinatown. Where is the only Chinatown in North America that is larger than the one in Vancouver? When did the Chinese begin to come to

Vancouver? As a group, would you call them a Johnny-come-lately to the city?

The "problem" from the perspective of many long-established residents of the city is that the new Hong Kong Chinese are very wealthy and not content to confine their locational choices within the traditional areas that Asian immigrants have lived in the past. For these nouveau riche Chinese, nothing less than the best neighborhood in the city will do. What is that neighborhood? Click on *Find* and then *Places* and type in Vancouver. Now click on the *Web Links* and open to the Web site entitled *Expedia World Guide--Vancouver*. Within the site click on the *Neighborhoods* option and scroll down to the West Side. As with many American cities, Vancouver's neighborhoods are defined by occupational, demographic, and income characteristics. Working class, blue collar neighborhoods are on the east side of town (e.g., East Van) while the upscale neighborhoods are on the West Side. Young affluent professionals (i.e., Yuppies) might opt for a condo in Kitsilano for example. This is the neighborhood from which the environmental activist group Greenpeace first got its start. But the really ritzy neighborhood is Shaughnessy Heights, a leafy paradise of fine homes with views of the inlet and parks. Traditionally, the makeup of the neighborhood was very Anglo; many of the elderly residents tracing their ancestry many generations back to the United Kingdom. The Hong Kong Chinese that are moving into the area often tear down half-timbered English Tudor style houses and replace them with bold showcase houses, the "footprint" of which takes up practically the entire lot leaving very little, if any, green space. Whereas before the house might have had 3,500 square feet of living space, it's successor may be more in the 12,000 square feet class. Long-time residents of the neighborhood claim they aren't being racist, but rather that these garish new upstart "monster houses" ruin the quiet, genteel look of the neighborhood. What do you think? What difference might it have made if these very wealthy Chinese had remained in the International District (i.e., Chinatown) located closer to the downtown area?

In 1975, after the United States left Vietnam, many persons fearful of retribution by the Communist North Vietnamese that took over the country, fled to other nearby countries. Many placed themselves in harm's way by plying the sometimes-treacherous waters of the South China Sea in rickety, makeshift boats. They were referred to as the "boat people" and their plight drew worldwide attention as some of their neighbors were unwilling to grant them political asylum. Was the departure of Hong Kong's "yacht people" really necessary? Let's see what Hong Kong's official answer is. Click on *Find* and then on *Countries* and type in *Hong Kong*. Look at the map of the autonomous state of Hong Kong, for the foreseeable future to be treated as a Special Administrative Region (SAR) of China and granted a great deal of local autonomy. Of course China acceded to these conditions with the British in the historic accords that were worked out between the two nations. Prior to July 1997, Britain had a 99-year lease on the colony. Why do you think China acceded and is downplaying its authority to control events in Hong Kong? Click on the sidebar to go to *Web Sites* for Hong Kong. One, called *Hong Kong in*

Transition 1997 and Beyond, is an official source and tries to dispel rumors and myths about the "one country, two systems" philosophy. It appears that this philosophy has really been embraced by the new Chinese leadership, but time will tell. Within the Web site, click on *Common Misconceptions*. This is the official response to a series of valid concerns that Hong Kong residents might have had about the takeover. The misconceptions of most importance to the wealthy who have fled Hong Kong for overseas destinations such as Vancouver, are encapsulated in the sections called *Economic and Financial Issues* and *Monetary Issues*. The worries are expressed as a series of myths which are, in reality, the candid and valid concerns expressed by many of the Chinese expatriates. To counter each myth is a statement of official policy and/or something proactive that Chinese officials have already implemented to remedy imbalances.

Suppose for a minute that you are a wealthy Hong Kong industrialist who is still contemplating a move to Vancouver or elsewhere within the Pacific Realm. After reading the official responses to these concerns (i.e., the myths), would you be convinced that you could conduct your business as it was when Hong Kong was a British dependency? Why or why not? Do you think the recent downturn in stock markets and currency devaluations throughout much of Southeast Asia has anything to do with the Chinese takeover of Hong Kong? Why or why not?

Keywords: Vancouver, Hong Kong, overseas Chinese, "yacht people"

Large Map, Small Scale;
Small Map, Large Scale

One of the most confusing aspects of cartography is
the professional's use of the phrase large (or small)
scale compared with the layperson's conventional
usage of the same terms. To the layperson, if a map
depicts a large area of the earth's surface, say an
entire continent, that is a large- scale map. By the
same token, a plat map of a suburban subdivision
would be a small-scale map because the total area
depicted is relatively small.

That is decidedly NOT how the cartographer or
geographer defines the term "scale". To the
geographic professional, scale is a fraction or a ratio
of what one inch on the map represents in terms of
the number of inches on the earth's surface. If one
inch on the map represented say, 1000 inches on the
ground, the cartographer would call that a large-scale
map because the fraction 1/1,000 is large relative to a
map in which one-inch might represent 250,000
inches on the ground. The fraction in the latter case
(1/250,000) is a smaller fraction (i.e., closer to zero)
and the map is said to be small scale.

Let's use the tools available in Encarta to reinforce
this point. When *Encarta* first boots up, click on
View the World. What you should see is a spherical
representation of the earth as if viewed by a satellite

or space ship hundreds of miles above the surface of the earth. We use the term "representation" because it is literally impossible to portray the spherical earth surface on a flat, two-dimensional map without sacrificing direction, shape, or distance (or some combination of two or more of those critical aspects). The Mercator projection, for example, distorts the polarward extensions of the map so that Greenland appears as large as all of South America--when in fact it is only about one-seventh its size. And yet, the Mercator projection is still very useful for navigational charts because a straight line can represent the shortest route between two points. Let's see if map scale differences and the nature of the shortest path between two points can be illustrated using Encarta. With the map still at the small scale (i.e., with the approximately 9 centimeters (cm) long legend bar equaling 6,000 kilometers (km)), place the mouse on the smaller map of the world in the upper left-hand corner of the image on the screen. See how adept you are at holding your finger on the mouse and dragging it on that world map until you have the "cross hairs" of the map centered on the Caspian Sea in the former Soviet Union. Once you have the map centered on the Caspian use the *Magnifying Glass* at the bottom left to magnify (the magnifying glass with the plus on it) the same area. What is the scale now? We can note that the legend bar (about nine centimeters in length) now represents 3,000 km rather than the 6,000 km in the previous representation. Does that make this map a larger scale than its predecessor?

Every time we click on the magnifying glass we are honing in on an increasingly smaller area on the ground and thus we are viewing a progressively larger scale map. At the scales, when the legend bar equaled either 6,000 km or 3,000 km, what was the title of the map? How does the title change when you click on the magnifying glass again and increase the scale so that only 1,500 km appears on the legend bar? What happens when the scale is doubled again by clicking once more on the magnifying glass (i.e., when the legend bar equals 800 km)? This time the title of the map should have remained the same as previously. What happens to the map title when the scale is enlarged once again. At this point the 9-cm legend bar represents 300 km. What is that scale expressed as a ratio? (Hint: In order to resolve this we have to express both the map and map scale in comparable units. How many centimeters are there in a kilometer? How many centimeters of earth surface space is, therefore, represented by one centimeter on the map? That will be the map ratio).

Now let's experiment with another tool contained on Encarta. Restore the map to its world scale again (with at least 3000 km shown on the legend bar). Using the *Hand* symbol, rotate the globe by dragging your mouse as if you were actually running your fingers over a globe in the classroom. Rotate until you can clearly view both sides of the Pacific Rim (i.e., so that Japan and China are on the left-hand side and California on the right). Now, suppose you wanted to fly the most direct route from San Francisco, California to Seoul, Korea. Make sure you know approximately where your origin and destination points are located before proceeding. Now, pull down the menu at the top of the screen called *Tools*. Within the *Tools* utility, click on the

Measure Tool. Locate San Francisco and click on it as the origin. Now find *Seoul* and click on it as the destination. How far is it (in kilometers) from San Francisco to Seoul? What island group would you fly over to get there? Does this surprise you? Why or why not? How would you describe the shape of the pathway between San Francisco and Seoul? When a pilot talks about a Great Circle Route do you think you understand what that means now?

Keywords: map scale, Mercator projection, Great Circle Routes

Postcards From Encarta: Wish You Were Here!

Part III of this chapter focuses on "Regional Imagery," and asks you to collect postcards that are representative of the region in which you live. When you tackled that assignment, you may have been surprised by how others view the place where you live. If you read the fine print on the back of most postcards, you probably noted that often the photographers, artists, and publishers are not from your hometown and more often than not may not even live in your country. Were you surprised by the images that postcard publishers chose to represent your region? Did you learn anything from the captions on the back of the postcards or did you find any editorial errors? Did they overlook anything you would have like to see memorialized on a postcard?

Now here is your chance to project the image of your region and interpret other cultural regions as well. Imagine yourself the CEO of a postcard company and for your pet project you have decided to establish an entire line of geographic postcards based on Joel Garreau's, "Nine Nations of North America." Using Figure 2.2 "The Nine Nations of North America, a newspaper journalist's perceptual regions," in your text as a guide, you will create a series of original postcards to represent each of the vernacular regions. To begin planning for your postcards, go to Encarta and create a map of *North America* using the *Find Places* tool. Using Figure 2.2 in your text as your guide, approximate the locations of each region by clicking on the upper left corner of the region's boundary and drawing a box on the map. Click to zoom in on the region and create a new map. The new map won't have the exact boundaries as Figure 2.2 but you should try to include as much of the region as possible. Or, if you wish, you can go directly to states, provinces or countries within the regions and view the slides in *Sights and Sounds*. If you choose this approach, just be sure the locations depicted in the images correspond with the geographic boundaries of Garreau's regions.

Scan through *Sights and Sounds* for each of the *Nine Nations* and single out one image that you would most closely associate with that cultural region. Print off the image and write your own caption. Be as creative as you like. Do not use the captions from Encarta. Rather, come up with your own interpretation of the image.

You can review the slides in *Sights and Sounds* for each of the following of Garreau's perceptual regions. When you come to the region in which you live, *select not one but two images* which you believe is most representative--the type of picture you would most likely want to send as a postcard.

Ecotopia	*The Empty Quarter*
MexAmerica	*The Bread-Basket*
Quebec	*The Foundry*
Dixie	*New England*
The Islands	

You should have a collection of 10 postcards when you have completed this activity. Would the postcards you selected really say to the recipient "Wish You Were Here?" or do you think the message would be, "Be Glad You Are Someplace Else?"

Keywords: culture region, Joel Garreau, Nine Nations of North America, postcards, perceptual region, vernacular region

Digging to Chinatown:
Relocation Diffusion in Action

Have you ever wondered how ethnic neighborhoods
are established? Why are some sections of cities
dominated by one culture group while other
neighborhoods seem more defined in other ways? A
look to ethnic neighborhoods will give you some
insight as the end result of relocation diffusion, chain
migration, and segregation.

When someone mentions "Chinatown," what location
first springs to mind? If you first thought of San
Francisco it might be because you live in that region
or have seen this neighborhood depicted in the
media. If you live in or near British Columbia, your
vision of Chinatown would be in Vancouver, the
second-largest Chinese community in North America
after San Francisco. Or if you call Australia home,
the city of Brisbane may come to mind. Let's take a
look at all these of these "Chinatowns" and through
Encarta explore the diffusion dynamics that resulted
in the creation of these distinct ethnic neighborhoods.
Before we begin our virtual tour, take a few minutes
and read *Human Migration* in *World Themes*. You
can access this narrative by clicking on *Find World
Themes*.

The first stop on our tour of Chinatowns is San
Francisco. Create a map of the city using the *Find*

Places tool. The result should be a street and area map of San Francisco. Now click on *Geography* and read a short summary of the city's history. When did the city begin receiving immigrants from China? Why would San Francisco have been their most logical destination? Go back to the map of the city and find Chinatown. You can click on *Chinatown* to get a close up look at the streets of San Francisco. Next, go to *Sights and Sounds* and select the slide titled *Chinatown, San Francisco.* If this photo lacked this caption, would you have known you were in the United States?

Our second stop on our Chinatown tour is Vancouver, British Columbia. Go to a map of this city using the *Find Places* option. Click on *Geography* and read a short history of the city then select *Sights and Sounds* and view the slide titled Vancouver's Thriving Chinatown. What attracted Chinese immigrants to the Vancouver area in the 19th century? Is this similar to the "pull factors" that brought the first groups of Asian immigrants to San Francisco?

Our final stop on our world tour of Chinatown neighborhoods is Brisbane, Australia. Bring up a map of the city using the *Find Places* option and use *Geography* to read some background information. Next, go to *Sights and Sounds* to view the image titled, *Chinatown in Brisbane.* How is this slide similar or different from the previous two Chinatowns you have toured? How do you suppose "Fortitude Valley" earned its name? What locational similarities does this Chinatown share with those of San Francisco and Vancouver in respect to their respective downtowns? Why do you think this pattern emerged?

Why do you think Chinatowns have survived for over 100 years? Do you think these neighborhoods persist today as foci for Asian immigration and culture?

Keywords: migration, diffusion, Chinatown, San Francisco, Vancouver, Brisbane

Kuby, et al.
Chapter 4: Newton's First Law of Migration: The
Gravity Model

A Matter of Some Gravity: World Population Cores and Distance Decay

The book does a wonderful job of illustrating the gravity formulation based on Newton's law of the attraction of heavenly bodies. In the Newtonian formulation, the exponent to which distance is raised is two (i.e., the relationships are distance squared ones). In more pragmatic applications, variants of the classic gravity formulation have been developed to forecast forms of human interaction. This interaction can include, but is not limited to, the migration of people, the movement of commodities and even the selection of marriage partners. Instead of distance being squared in the denominator of the classical gravity formulation, the exponent to which distance is raised is sometimes treated as a parameter to be fitted—the lower the exponent value the less the frictional effect of distance on that form of interaction and vice versa.

What can *Encarta* do to illustrate the gravity model given that large scale subnational data are not readily available (although they might be tapped from appropriate *Web Links* as shown in other activities throughout this *Pocket Guide*)? How about simply confirming whether a gradation of population from key core areas at the world scale is really visible? If so, such confirmation should lend credence to the extraordinary power of the deceptively simple gravity formulation. Clicking on *View the World*, pull down the *Map Styles* tool and go to *Satellite* and then to *Earth at Night.* This dramatic map is really a composite of many satellite images taken on various clear evenings so that cloud cover is at a minimum throughout the globe and it is night time everywhere simultaneously. The most obvious features on the map are the lights of the urban conurbations from giant behemoths like New York or Tokyo or Mexico City to smaller cities and towns dotting the landscape. The distribution of population void areas (the dark patches on the satellite image) speaks volumes about where people are not, just as the light patches tell us where they are. Does the pattern of human settlement throughout the world in any way illustrate the gravity model? We think you'll find that it does although it helps to know a little about the settlement history, the resource base, and the barriers to human settlement to really understand the distribution of world population.

Dragging your mouse to move the globe, center the globe on Europe and then use the *Magnifying Glass* to increase the geographic scale (the legend bar should show either 3,000 km or 1,500 km). Would you say that Europe has a core area? Where is it exactly? The Dutch call this area the Randstat and it consists of Europe's largest deep water port of Rotterdam in addition to Amsterdam and several other large cities which have coalesced together into a major conurbation. As you can see, the core area seems to extend across the English Channel to include the United Kingdom as well. Where within the United Kingdom is the core area centered? The core area extends into the former West Germany and a heavy industrial area known as the Rhine-Ruhr Basin. Can you find that portion of the European core? Beyond the core, the population density seems to decrease with increasing distance from it just as the gravity model would predict. There are, however, some significant outliers--large places or conurbations that are not contiguous with the core. The Paris Basin in north central France seems to be one such outlier. Can you name some others within Europe? Why do you think that population is concentrated at these outlier nodes?

Now, spin the globe (by dragging the mouse) and focus on Asia. Why do you think that Japan with its approximately 125 million people stands out so brightly whereas China with almost ten times its population appears only modestly lit? When we move away from the coastal areas and the river valleys of China, the bright lights become almost nonexistent. Why is that?

Finally, spin the globe so that it is centered on North Africa, specifically on Egypt. What is unusual about the pattern of population in Egypt? What factors account for this concentration and unusual distribution? Cairo is Africa's largest city with over 10 million people in the greater metropolitan area. Can you spot it easily on the nighttime satellite image? Several years ago, the geographer Waldo Tobler thought that satellite imagery might be used to conduct a type of census and he used Egypt to illustrate his method. Like the gravity model, Tobler based his model on a natural law too. In his case, the law pertained mainly to living organisms and comes from the field of biology. It is called the law of allometric growth. Simply stated, the law argues that the growth of an organism's limbs and organs is proportional to the overall growth of the organism. Hand and feet don't just suddenly start growing faster than the rest of the body. The entire body grows in a proportional manner. Using this law, Tobler was able to relate the size of the built-up urban area as a surrogate for the actual population living there. Of course, a distance decay effect was assumed with more people living in the central area of the cities and the density of populations tapering off near the periphery. Applying this natural law to the distribution of Egypt's population, Tobler estimated the population of the country within the acceptable degree of error of the official census that cost millions of dollars to conduct. Tobler's method cost mere hundreds at the most—a real boon to financially strapped third world countries who might find it difficult and expensive to conduct a thorough census. Do you think a census conducted using Tobler's method would be as accurate in the rainforests of Sumatra as it was in the desert of Egypt? Why or why not?

Is it comforting for you to know that human behavior (in the aggregate anyway) is so predictable that natural laws such as Newton's law of gravitation or the biological law of allometric growth do a remarkably good job of predicting our behavior? Does it make you want to rebel against the norm just so you will not be considered so predictable? Would your capricious, aberrant behavior really do much to change the fundamental nature of these natural laws or their sociological and geographical derivatives? Are you a residual (i.e., outlier) in the grand scheme of things or a well-explained case? If geographers can predict your spatial behavior with a remarkable degree of accuracy, does that prediction in any way deny your free will to act as you want to?

Keywords: gravity model, law of allometric growth, Egypt, Waldo Tobler, satellite imagery, core area, urban agglomerations (conurbations)

Kuby, et al.
Chapter 5: Trapped in Space: Space-Time Prisms and
Individual Activity Space

My Prism Can Be My Prison

The notion of time-geography, the very choreography of our existence, is a fairly new one first discussed by Törsten Hägerstrand and his Swedish associates in the 1970s. It was that group of geographers who saw great potential in charting the daily life path of the average citizen. Once you get beyond the technical jargon involving space-time prisms, space-time paths, coupling constraints, dioramas and the like, the concept is a fairly simple one--you can't be in two different places at the same time. And, furthermore there may be opportunity costs foregone because of our relative immobility. When daily logs were kept, we learned that working class people may be more constrained by their time-space prism (prison?) than their upper middle class counterparts because they lack access to high speed mobility systems. We have also learned that there are gender and age-related differences that can make a person relatively confined to a limited geographic space. For example, a young wife with several pre-school children might be precluded by economic circumstance or personal preference from participating in many of the activities going on outside the home.

These concepts, while important, are individualistic and difficult if not impossible to illustrate using *Encarta Virtual Globe*. But, the related concept of the time-space convergence, first introduced into the geographic literature by Donald Janelle, can certainly be illustrated using Encarta. In an early (1932) historical atlas of the United States, the historian Charles O. Paullin and the geographer John K. Wright developed an interesting series of maps to illustrate the speed that a message could move into the interior of the country at three different time periods. The earliest time period chosen was 1800. At this time, overland travel was very expensive, arduous, and slow. On the other hand, sailing ships plied the waters between port cities in the United States bringing cotton from Charleston, South Carolina to Boston in exchange for shoes or woolen goods. Thus cities along the eastern seaboard were interconnected. In 1800, it would have taken a full six weeks for a message or a shipment of commodities to reach what was to become the city of Chicago at the southern tip of Lake Michigan. At the time, the area was known as Fort Dearborn, military outpost designed to protect fur traders and other hardy souls in that region against attacks by hostile Indian tribes in the area. By 1830, the steam engine had been added to packet boats that plied the navigable inland waterways opening up vast hinterland trade areas for expansion. Especially important was the opening of the Erie Canal in 1825. This canal opened up a sea level route from the port of New York into the Great Lakes system via the Hudson and Mohawk Rivers that formed a corridor throughout upstate New York. The steam engine led to the growth of cities along the corridor such as Rochester, Utica, Troy and Schenectady. Despite the advances in technology, it still took three weeks for a letter or a shipment of commodities to reach Chicago. The city of Chicago was incorporated three years later and by the 1880s was the second largest city in the United States. In 1857, the last year examined by Wright and Paullin, the first railroad bridge across the Mississippi had been constructed, the first transcontinental railroads with a standardized gauge of track was less than a decade away and a message from New York could now reach Chicago in only two days. The interesting isochronal maps (i.e., showing lines of equal travel time away from New York City) of the historical atlas, edited by Wright and Paullin, illustrate well the time-space convergence. From six weeks in 1800 to three weeks in 1830 to two days in 1857 a message could be sent from New York to Chicago .

Now click on *Find Places* in Encarta and type in *New York*. Using the mouse to drag the map around a bit, making sure that New York City is approximately in the middle of a map in which the legend bar goes to 80 km. This is what a driver for overland transportation system would have had to face in 1800. What are some of the barriers to movement overland that a driver would have to face? What physical features are located west and northwest of the city? The areal extent of the map is about as far as one could go in two or three days in a horse-drawn wagon.

Now, using the *Magnifying Tool*, click on the *Minus Icon* so that the map is still centered on New York City but the map legend now extends 150 kms. According to Wright and Paullin, the time it took to go from point A to B was halved between 1800 and 1830. Thus, a steam packet or improved overland vehicle such as the iron horse, could travel to the places shown on this map in two-three days. To what states does the map at this scale reach? The time-space convergence sped up between 1830 and 1857 much more rapidly than it did in the 1800-1830 era. Now click the *Magnifying Glass* (negative sign) twice such that the legend extends to 800 km. Chicago is now at the periphery of the region shown on the map taking two to three day delivery time as it did in 1857. What are the most far-flung states from New York that can still be reached in two days? In less than sixty years, the convergence went from 80 km in a fixed time period (2-3 days) to 800 km, a tenfold speeding up (convergence) process. Did your neck snap in the process due to the G forces? Can you think of improvements in transportation and communication technology that have contributed to the space-time convergence that we have experienced in our affluent and developed country?

Keywords: space-time prisms, time-space convergence, time-geography, Törsten Hägerstrand, Donald Janelle

Around the World From
Pre- to Post-Industrial

Figure 6.1 in the text has been used to illustrate how
a particular country such as the United States had
made the transition from an agrarian society to a
post-industrial one. In the early years of the United
States' history, the economy was heavily dependent
on the primary sector of the economy--the jobs that
are directly reliant upon raw materials from the earth
or sea. Later, manufacturing (i.e., the secondary
sector of the economy involving the change of those
raw materials into more useful products thus adding
value to them in the process) became the backbone of
American emergence as a world economic power.
Now, the United States is in a post-industrial phase in
which the service industries (both the more routine
tertiary sector and the higher-order and more highly
professional quaternary sector) are dominating the
jobs Americans perform. So, Figure 6.1 can be
interpreted in a longitudinal sense for a particular
country's economic transition. But, can the diagram
also be used in a cross-sectional sense? That is, for a
particular time period, would we be able to find
different countries in the world at different stages in
this transition? If so, could the stage a country finds
itself in be used as an indicator of level of economic
development? Let's use Encarta to find out. We'll
focus on five countries that are at different stages of
development: Bangladesh, a desperately poor country

in south Asia that some development experts have even labeled a "fourth world basket case" because of its seemingly intractable problems. Then, let's focus on Thailand, a third world country in southeast Asia that is currently emerging from its traditional roots to become a very fast-paced economy. The third place to examine is Brazil, a huge country with a great, albeit spotty, natural resource base and development potential--a country that development experts refer to as a newly industrializing country (NIC).

Of course, we shouldn't overlook the United States and, for comparison, let's look at Switzerland, a country in Europe with a standard of living (as measured by per capita income) even higher than our own. Is their employment base that different from our own? Can we learn some lessons from Switzerland's obvious success? Using the *Find Places* option in Encarta, type in the names of each of these five countries and then click on the sidebar entitled *Facts and Figures*. Create a table by scrolling down the *Facts and Figures* section until you come to *Economy* and record the following information for each of the five countries: per capita GDP (gross domestic product), the proportion of the labor force engaged in agriculture (primary sector), industry (secondary sector), and services (tertiary and quaternary sectors). What appears to be the relationship between per capita income (GDP) and the percentage of the labor force engaged in agriculture? What is the most unusual aspect of Switzerland's economic structure? Only Botswana (yes, Botswana) has as high a percentage of its labor force engaged in manufacturing as Switzerland. What kind of manufacturing do the Swiss engage in? Let's take a closer look with Encarta. Using *Find*

Places, type in *Switzerland* and return to the *Facts and Figures* sidebar for a moment. What are Switzerland's three leading exports? Now click on the sidebar called *Sights and Sounds* and click on the slide entitled *Making watches in Switzerland*. Where within Switzerland are most of the fine time pieces made? Sometimes a time honored tradition of craftsmanship can negatively impact market share. Before 1960, some 90 percent of the watches in the world used Swiss movements. It was, in fact, the Swiss who invented and developed the prototype for a quartz watch. But that technology did not fit into the methods then used to produce watches in Switzerland and the right to fabricate and commercialize the quartz watch was sold to the Japanese government. Because of the close alliance of business and government in Japan leading some detractors to call it "Japan, Inc.", soon Japanese watchmakers such as Seiko, Citizen, and Pulsar were dominating the world market for watches. Japanese watches are reliable and inexpensive. Swiss watches are wonderfully crafted, reliable and expensive. The Swiss fought back with the Swatch watch, a quartz watch produced in many designer colors and patterns but have never regained the market share they once enjoyed. Now click on the sidebar called *Society* and then click on the section called *Economy*. What country is Switzerland's most important trading partner? Can you think of another country that might fit the opening statement in the Economy section, "Despite a lack of natural resources, Switzerland has a strong economy?"

Reflect for a moment on the difference between the economies of the United States and Switzerland. The

110

United States used to have a stronger industrial base than it does now. Many of the former domestic manufacturing jobs have been outsourced to third world countries where the products can be produced at much lower costs than they can be produced in the United States largely because of the labor cost differential between the United States and the third world. Why aren't Swiss manufacturers outsourced to the same degree? Switzerland, like Germany and many other European countries, has a very strong program of craftsperson apprenticeships. Should such programs be implemented in the United States? Why or why not?

Keywords: economic sector, gross domestic product, Bangladesh, Thailand, Brazil, United States, Switzerland, watches, manufacturing

Another Type of Egyptian Pyramid

You have undoubtedly seen pictures of the colossal pyramids at Giza in Egypt, one of the seven wonders of the ancient world and still a major tourist destination despite recent terrorist attacks. But there is another pyramid that looms large in the minds of many Egyptian planners and government officials—the demographic pyramid (i.e., age-sex cohort diagrams). These diagrams are usually referred to as pyramids even though their shape can vary dramatically from that shape. Just look at the pyramid for Spain, a country that now possesses the lowest birth rate of any European country (incredible for a country that is nominally Roman Catholic) as pictured in Figure 7. 4. Only those age-sex cohort diagrams for the Philippines and Zaire (now the Democratic Republic of the Congo) look very pyramid-like with a broad base and a tapering apex.

What about Egypt? Wouldn't it be ironic if it's age-sex cohort resembled the Great Pyramids at Giza? If it did, what would be the long-term consequences of such a shape? Let's turn to *Encarta* to learn more about the fascinating land of Egypt and some of the ways it has come to terms with its extremely high physiologic density (i.e., the number of people per unit of arable land). Since most of the land area of Egypt is desert, the population of over 62 million is forced to live along the Nile River floodplain, its tributaries, a few oases, and the delta it forms with the Mediterranean. The Nile is truly Egypt's life blood and has been over the millenia.

Using the *Find Places* command in Encarta type in *Egypt*. First let's examine some demographic data pertaining to Egypt by clicking on *Map Styles* and then clicking on *Statistical*. Within the data sets contained therein, click on the one marked *Population*. Unfortunately, data on crude birth rate and crude death rate are not available for Egypt. If they were, we might have been able to determine what stage of the demographic transition Egypt falls into. But there are other data you can record and compare with nearby countries in the region of north Africa and southwestern Asia. Click on and record the value of the following population variables for Egypt: *Fertility Rate (1990); Population Growth Rate (1990); Population Growth Rate, Urban (1990); Population Aged Infant to 14 (1995); and Population Aged 65 and Older (1995)*. If you haven't done so, notice where within the data array, the values for Egypt fall (of the countries reporting data). That's right. Egypt is just about smack dab in the middle. For a country with a large population base to begin with, that is a good place to be. We're sure that many Egyptian planners and government officials wish that rate of natural increase were even lower than it is now. But, Egypt has lower rates of increase, lower fertility rates (although five children per woman of childbearing years still seems quite high by Western standards), lower rates of juvenility (i.e., a dependent population less than 15 years of

113

age) and higher rates of elderly persons than many of its surrounding neighbors.

Keeping with the cliché that a picture is worth a thousand words, let's look at Egypt more closely. Click on the sidebar marked *Sights and Sounds* and you will be treated to at least four different types of music. Focus first on the slide entitled *Egyptian Farmland*. If it weren't for a government edict mandating that some food crops be grown, what crop would probably increase the most in acreage under production? Since land was recently expropriated from wealthy landholders and redistributed to the peasant farmers, what is the average sized holding in Egypt? Now turning to the slide called *Nile River at Aswan*, please answer the following questions. When was the Aswan High dam completed? Why was it built? Did its construction allow Egypt to add to its arable land resource base? What antiquities had to be moved as a result of the dam's construction and the subsequent submergence of previously dry land? According to the slide entitled *Farming in the Nile River Delta* what percentage of Egypt's population farms for their livelihood? What factors account for Egypt's high agricultural productivity? The caption to *Windswept Desert* says what Egypt's annual naturally-occurring rainfall is. What is it? Focusing on the *Aswan High Dam*, what large body of water was created south of the dam? Who or what is Nassar? What have been the benefits (if any) of building the high dam on the Nile? What are the negative consequences (if any)? How old is the *Great Pyramid at Giza*? How many stone blocks were used to build it? At the *Al Fayyum Oasis*, we are introduced to a different type of extractive activity—aquaculture. How does the aquaculture practiced at Birkat Qarun differ from catfish farming in Mississippi or tilapia ponds in southeastern Asia? How is the salinity level kept relatively constant? We can't let you miss the *Giza Sphinx*. From what material was it created? How long ago? In the slide simply called *Village Life along the Nile* it is stated that "Rural life is dependent upon the contributions of family members." If there is no national system of social security or old age pensions, would this be a reason why the fertility rate is still relatively high? In the slide *Expansive Lake Nassar* we see once again the potential environmental consequence of building a 300 km. lake in a desert environment. Why do you think that simple evaporation is such a concern? Finally, take a sweeping view of the largest city in Africa—the *Metropolis of Cairo*. What is your general impression of the city based on that photograph? Is Cairo the future for a country that is now 80 percent rural?

Keywords: fertility rate, population pyramids (age-sex cohorts), Egypt, Aswan High Dam, Lake Nassar, Nile River

Kuby, et al.
Chapter 8: From Rags to Riches: The Dimensions of
Development

Ecotourism: It Isn't Easy Being Green--But it Can Be Profitable

Picture this. You've worked hard all year long and are ready to take advantage of the vacation time you have coming to you. Where do you go? Disney World? No! You opt for two weeks of trekking through the tropical vegetation somewhere in Latin America to help save the rainforest. Huh? That's right. You are an ecotourist and are more than willing to pay serious money to do anything but relax in some of the world's most fragile and threatened environments. Why would you rather commune with tarantualas than take a ride on Space Mountain? Well, maybe you have a fear of heights, or maybe you are part of a growing number of people from more developed countries (MDCs) joining a global movement toward ecotourism. What is ecotourism and what is its role in economic development? Let's find out.

Ecotourism is one facet of sustainable development as discussed on pages 8-8 and 8-9 in your text. For a definition of ecotourism, go to *Encarta* and use the *Find Content* tool. When you enter *Ecotourism* you should come up with a list of five items, the first of which is a definition of ecotourism in the glossary. Read the description of ecotourism. You might want to print this out for future reference. You should also keep this list open by clicking on the box at the lower

left-hand corner of the *Find Content* window. You
can click and drag on this window to set it aside for
later use. Like now.

Look at the four locations listed under ecotourism in
the *Find Content* box. Go to each of these sites and
become a virtual ecotourist.

Papua New Guinea
When you "arrive" in Papua New Guinea, read *Land
and Climate* to get a feel for the environment. Why
would ecotourists be attracted to this location? For
more information, click on *Web Links*. First, find out
what conditions visitors may encounter by selecting
*U.S. State Department Travel Advisory for Papua
New Guinea*. Next, go to the *Destination Papua New
Guinea* Web site. After reviewing this page, which
aspects of Papua New Guinea would appeal to you
and which would make you think twice about being
an ecotourist in this Pacific nation?

St. Kitts & Nevis
Welcome to the Caribbean and the beautiful volcanic
islands of St. Kitts and Nevis. As a curious
ecotourist, you would want to read about the *Land
and Climate* of the region. After reviewing this
section, why would the government of St. Kitts and
Nevis want to encourage ecotourism? Now go to
Web Links and look at two sites, *Official Guide to St.
Kitts and Nevis*, and *U.S. State Department Travel
Advisory for St. Kitts and Nevis*. Based on this
information, do you think the islands are a good
location to promote ecotourism? Why would you
want to go to St. Kitts or why would you skip this

location as an ecotourist in favor or an alternative destination?

Suriname

As an ecotourist in Suriname, you would want to read about the country's *Land and Climate*. What are some of the unique environmental features of Suriname? Why would the government look to ecotourism as a way to protect natural resources? Go to *Web Links* and click on **Destination Suriname** and *U.S. State Department Travel Advisory*. What cultural and environmental features would prove attractive to ecotourists?

Islas de la Bahia

You've just set foot on Islas de la Bahia, and island off the coast of Honduras. What do you see? Take a ferry back to the mainland and explore Honduras as well. You can go to a map of Honduras and click on *Web Links* for details about tourism in the region. Go to *Destination Honduras* and *U.S. State Department Travel Advisory for Honduras* for more information. What sort of health risks might you encounter as an ecotourist in Honduras? Why would you want to carry bottled water with you everywhere you go? Would a Honduran dog be an ecotourist's best friend? How might ecotourism prevent the development of a Honduran "desert"?

Now that you are an experienced virtual ecotourist, which of these destinations would you prefer if you were to take a trip in real life? Rank each of the four locations in order of preference and explain why you chose one over the other. After reviewing all the material, why do you think ecotourism is a popular economic development tool and do you think it really works to protect the environment? Is it going to be easy for these countries to stay green?

Keywords: ecotourism, Papua New Guinea, St. Kitts and Nevis, Suriname, Islas de la Bahia, Honduras, environment

Kuby, et al.
Chapter 9: Take Me Out to the Ball Game: Market
Areas and the Urban Hierarchy

Towns in Iowa: Central Places and a Whole Lot More!

As you might be able to gather from some of the studies cited in Chapter 9, Iowa is considered the classic central place testing ground. It is relatively flat to gently rolling. While not the isotropic plain of the classical theory it comes pretty darn close--except for the slightly more rugged northeastern part of the state that is part of the Driftless Area, a region missed by the most recent glaciation. What does the glaciated landscape of Iowa look like? You can find out by clicking on *Find Places* and typing in *Iowa*. Then go to the sidebar marked *Sights and Sounds* and you will see two slides of the Iowa landscape. The first is a typical farming scene (*Iowa's Riches*). Note how flat the land is in all directions. What crop do you think the farmer is driving his tractor through? If you said soybeans you would be right. Soybeans are now second only to corn in importance to the state. Soybean acreage has increased steadily since the 1940s in Iowa eclipsing hay and oats to become the second leading agricultural crop. Why? Because soybeans have a relatively short growing season, as a legume they produce their own nitrogen fertilizer fixed by bacteria that attach themselves to the roots of the plant, they have dozens of uses from meat extender to cattle feed, they have never been subject to an acreage allotment, and there is a huge foreign market for soybeans and soy products in the Pacific

Rim. The second slide shows an area of Iowa close to the floodplain of the Mississippi River in the eastern part of the state (*Mississippi Farmland*) where the effect of glaciation during the most recent Ice Age is quite apparent.

Certainly glaciation is one reason for the look of the land in the state of Iowa but there is another factor that has also had a profound effect on the settlement pattern of the state—the township and range survey system. This survey system was used to divide the state into political units called townships and counties as part of the Northwest Ordinance Survey of 1785. This was long before Iowa was granted statehood (1849) and long before very many people lived there. Iowa was simply part of the Northwest Territories, territories north of the Ohio River. How can something as seemingly mundane as how land parcels are platted on maps even before any significant population lives there affect the distribution of central places? The typical county was square in shape consisting of 16 townships. A township, in turn, consisted of 36 one square mile parcels of land called sections. A section of land (i.e., one square mile) consists of 640 acres. During the Homestead Act of 1862, parcels of land not yet settled (mostly in the northwestern part of the state—the last to be settled) were allocated to people who wished to farm the land in quarter sections (160 acre parcels). So, the average farm size was about 160 acres (one-quarter section). All of the farm-to-market roads were oriented along the township and range boundaries. You didn't want to cut across a farmer's acreage if at all possible. Every township declared one centrally located section as set aside for the one-room school and other township functions. Likewise, every county seat town was centrally located within the county boundaries. Since there are 99 counties in the state, one might assume that the 99 largest cities would be the regularly spaced county seat towns. And, for the most part,you would be correct. There is, of course, some degree of suburbanization around many of the larger cities which leads to a bit of clustering (i.e.,urban agglomeration) but still the most remarkable feature of the Iowa landscape would be the regularity of spacing of the major central places and, by implication, all levels of the central place hierarchy from the smallest hamlet to the state capital of Des Moines. But, you need to prove this regularity for yourself. Using the map of Iowa with the scale going to 150 kilometers, let's measure the distance between seven largest central places in the state and their nearest neighbor of the same order. Those seven are Des Moines, Cedar Rapids, Waterloo, Davenport (not labeled per se, but part of the Rock Island and Moline, Illinois Quad Cities area on the border of eastern Iowa and western Illinois), Sioux City, Council Bluffs (right across the river from the much larger Omaha, Nebraska) and Dubuque. For example, Cedar Rapids' nearest neighbor of comparable hierarchical rank is Waterloo. What is the distance that separates them? Use the *Tools* pull-down menu and click on *Measure Tool*. Place one end of the *Measure Tool* on *Cedar Rapids* and the other on *Waterloo* and record the straight-line distance (measured in kilometers that separates them). Your answer should be about 84.6 kms. Click the cross-hairs on the origin and again on the destination to take a reading. Now record the values for the other six pairs of cities and average the

122

result. If your average was around 120 kilometers, you did the exercise correctly. Why do you think that on average the distance between major centers in the eastern part of the state is less than that in the western part?

In southern Germany, Walter Christaller, the geographer responsible for first developing central place theory, found that the average spacing of his largest urban centers (excluding the regional Bavarian capital of Munich) was about 36 kilometers. How do you account for the differences between the results obtained by Christaller and your own? What kinds of central place goods and services might you expect to find only at the highest level of the central place hierarchy in Iowa? Brian Berry and his associates used hospitals to represent the town level function in their study of southwestern Iowa (Figure 9.1 in your textbook). What would you use to represent the city level?

Keywords: Iowa, Northwest Ordinance Survey, township and range survey system, Homestead Act, central place theory, glaciation, Driftless Area

Manhattan Transformation: The Suburban Roots of Harlem

When you think about the suburbs, places like King of Prussia, Pennsylvania or Tysons Corners, Virginia, may come to mind as good examples of "edge cities." Your authors highlight King of Prussia as an example of a former bedroom community that has emerged into major employment center in the Philadelphia area (Figure 10.3). Prior to the 1960s, King of Prussia was not much more than a small residential community dotted with dairy farms and orchards. The development of office parks, shopping malls, and interstates changed King of Prussia into an employment, shopping, residential, and entertainment destination.

When we think of suburbs like King of Prussia, we conjure up an image of tract homes, sprawl, speculation, amenities which constitute a high quality of life, and the automobile as the primary source of transportation. We also tend to think of the chief suburban American demographic as middle-class white families. But suburbs are much older than the automobile and much more culturally diverse. Not all suburbs are flourishing and not all appeal to traditional families. Some older inner ring suburbs are subject to social and infrastructural decay and are succumbing to the same economic problems as many inner cities.

Transportation innovations such as the streetcar changed the spatial structure of cities in the late 19th century. What's become of those suburbs and what are their functions today? One example of a pre-auto age suburb is Harlem, New York.

If you have a hard time imagining Harlem as farmland, you may also find it difficult to think of Harlem as a suburban community in Manhattan. Harlem's history is closely linked with the evolution of suburbs in the United States. Let's go to Harlem and learn more about its rich history and cultural heritage.

Using the *Find Places* option, create a map of Harlem. Now click on *Geography* and read a short description of the neighborhood. How did the Dutch treat the land they occupied in the 17th century? When did Harlem develop as a suburb of New York City? To learn more about the evolution of Harlem from farmland, go to *Web Links* and click on *Rough Guide to Upper Manhattan and Harlem*. Read the introduction to New York City then click on *Harlem, Hamilton Heights, and the North*. Review this brief description of the area then click on *Harlem* and *Around Harlem*. While most people perceive Harlem as an African-American neighborhood, what has been the ethnic evolution of the area? How did transportation affect the development of Harlem? Why did the neighborhood fall into decline? How has gentrification changed Harlem since the 1970s? How does this recent Harlem renaissance relate to the Langston Hughes' quote at the beginning of the *Harlem* page?

When you compare Harlem to suburbs that emerged during the 1960s, do you find they have anything in common? What cultural resources does Harlem have that make it a more favorable location for gentrification than suburbs like King of Prussia? Imagine it is 20 years from now. Which area do you think would be more economically and socially viable--King of Prussia or Harlem--and in which would you prefer to live?

Keywords: suburbs, King of Prussia, New York City, Manhattan, Harlem, gentrification, transportation , land use

I'll See Your Bernadette Devlin and Raise You an Ian Paisley

Most of you reading this weren't even born when the "Troubles" began in Northern Ireland (a.k.a. Ulster) in the 1960s. Nor does the title of the chapter activity mean much to you. Bernadette Devlin was a young firebrand member of parliament (MP) elected from a heavily Catholic section of Northern Ireland. Her nemesis was Ian Paisley, also an MP and a staunch Protestant loyalist. Northern Ireland is the smaller northern end of the island, a part of the larger United Kingdom that also includes England, Wales, and Scotland. The larger southern portion of the island on which Northern Ireland is located contains the Irish Free State (a.k.a. Eire) a country that is wholly independent of the United Kingdom. Most of the residents of Ireland are Roman Catholic. Most of the population of Northern Ireland owes its allegiance to the Church of England (e.g., Episcopalians as we call them in the United States). There are, however, significant Catholic minorities in the major cities of Ulster especially Belfast and Londonderry and along the southern border region near Eire.

Why, when Episcopalians and Roman Catholics in the United States are entering into dialogue about sharing the Eucharist and other forms of shared worship experiences in the spirit of Christian ecumenicalism, are Protestants and Catholics in Northern Ireland still shooting at each other? Good question. The simple answer is that they soon may not be if all parties agree to the Peace Accord recently brokered by President Clinton working with Tony Blair, the British Prime Minister, and representatives from Ireland (and even the political arm of the Irish Republican Army, Sinn Féin). But truces and partition lines have been in place in Northern Ireland since 1969. Catholics in Northern Ireland detest the presence of British troops in their neighborhoods ostensibly to keep the peace and Protestants certainly don't like the terrorist tactics of the Irish Republican Army (IRA). The IRA has disrupted commerce, killed people with car bombs, and generally wrecked havoc on the entire United Kingdom, not just Northern Ireland.

As with many arguments, the fight is over more than just religion. Catholics feel that are treated as second-class citizens in Northern Ireland. They claim that they are always the last to be hired and the first to be fired from any job. The geographer Frederick Boal has written about the Fall Road-Shankill divide in Belfast, Northern Ireland. This divide was designated as a barricaded truce line after 1969 and the open hostilities seemed to die down with the imposition of British troops sent to enforce the peace. South of the divide is the Catholic neighborhood of Clonard. To the north is the heavily Protestant neighborhood of Shankill. The segregation indices discussed in the chapter would certainly be able to demarcate this strong distinction. The Shankill neighborhood always displayed orange bunting and painted the curbs orange on July 12th. Using Encarta, let's find out why. Click on *Find Places* and type *Northern Ireland.* Now, click on the sidebar marked *Sights and Sounds* and click on the slide entitled *Children at an Orange March.* After reading the caption, describe in your own words the origins of the animosity of the Protestants for the Catholics and vice versa. An interesting *Web Link* included with Encarta is a link to the *Irish News.* This newspaper, published in Northern Ireland, is very pro-Catholic. Protestants, according to Boal's study, read the *Belfast Times* almost exclusively and Catholics read the *Irish News.* As of the time of this writing, the peace plan proposed by Prime Minister Tony Blair and endorsed by most, but not all, Catholic and Protestant groups tops all other news and may be the best chance yet for a lasting peace.

Now let's switch to a focus on the Republic of Ireland. Click on *Find Places* and then type in *Ireland.* The textual material in the sidebar labeled Society provides good background to the current situation. Click on that and then scroll down or click on the section called *Recent Decades* and read it carefully. What does the Gaelic phrase Sinn Féin mean? How long has Northern Ireland been separate from Ireland? How would most Irish citizens like to see the issue of Northern Ireland resolved? How do you personally think this festering debate, exacerbated by residential segregation, mutual distrust, and misunderstanding will eventually resolve itself? Keep your eyes open to the newspaper and follow the story closely. The last time an accord was almost reached, an act of IRA terrorism scotched the deal. Let's hope that for the sake of world peace this current accord may finally end the long-standing "Troubles" in Northern Ireland.

Keywords: Northern Ireland, Ireland, Roman Catholic, Protestant, residential segregation, Sinn Féin, Irish Republican Army

Timor or Less: Indonesia's Claim at Stake

Have you ever heard of Timor? Did you even know it was an island let alone where it might be? Does it seem that some places on earth are so far removed from you that what happens there has little or no impact on your life? Such is the case with Timor, an island that is divided into East and West Timor, is claimed by Indonesia. If these are the simple facts, the everyday realities of life in Timor are much more complex.

Go to map of Timor using the *Find Places* tool. Read a short description of the island by clicking on *Geography*. How is the settlement history of Timor reflected in its ethnic composition? How did the withdrawal of colonial powers make Timor vulnerable to exploitation from Indonesia? What role has the United Nations played in resolving human rights issues in East Timor?

Let's look further into the conflicts between Timor and Indonesia by going to *Web Links* and clicking on *Human Rights in Indonesia*. Concentrate your reading on the first three pages, but be sure to give the rest of the document a quick review. Next, go to the Web page titled *East Timor Human Rights* and click on *Most Recent Additions to Home Page*. Read to two reports dated 1/98 and 2/98 as well as the link titled *Violence by the State Against Women in East Timor*. Based on your review of these reports, answer the following questions:

- How would you describe the character of the current government of Indonesia?   What role does the military play in the government?

- Despite a rapidly expanding economy, why do social and economic disparities remain such a chronic problem in Indonesia?

- What examples of human rights abuses are cited in these articles? Do you see a common thread among them?

- What evidence is there of persecution in East Timor based on the residents' ethnicity and religion?

- Who is Bishop Belo and what role has he played in the East Timor conflict?

- How would you describe the status of women in East Timor? Why are they reluctant to report that they have been victims of crimes?   How would you describe the crimes of sexual assault against women in East Timor and how is the Indonesian military involved in these crimes?

After reading about conditions in Yugoslavia in Chapter 12 of your textbook, do you see any similarities or differences between the situation in southeastern Europe and Indonesia? Which region do you believe will be the first to find peace?   What role has geography played in the political fortunes of these areas? What do you think will have to happen before people become more concerned about Yugoslavia and Indonesia?

Keywords: Indonesia, Timor, East Timor, human rights, gender, political geography

How Would You Like Your Animals--Rare?
Vacancies at the World Zoo

Think of yourself as the zookeeper to the world, responsible for the welfare of everything from aardvarks to zebras. It would not take you long to figure out there is a colossal variety of animals on the planet, each with their own unique habitats, food requirements, and frailties. And as a good zoo manager, you would want to do an inventory of the earth's animals to find out where they live and how many species are walking, trotting, crawling, and swimming around. In your research you would also find that many animals are facing incredible odds competing with humans for resources and space and in most cases, the humans are winning the war. Where would you go to find the most endangered animals and what can be done to prevent their extinction? Let's use *Encarta* to zoo-m in on the issues.

The first thing you would want to do as manager of the world's zoo is to find out where the wildlife lives and which animals are most threatened. Go to a map of the world and under *Map Styles* select *Statistical*. Click on *Choose Statistic* and then select *Environment* as your category. For each of the following *World Stats*, list the countries that are ranked as the top five in each category.

Amphibian Species, Known
Amphibian Species, Threatened
Bird Species, Known
Bird Species, Threatened
Fish Species, Known
Fish Species, Threatened
Deforestation, Annual
Protected Land
Mammal Species, Known
Mammal Species, Threatened
Reptile Species, Known
Reptile Species, Threatened

Based on your initial research, answer the following questions. You may find it helpful to go to these countries via *Encarta* to read and view additional information. You can do this by using the *Find Places* tool and following the links for each country.

- What are the only categories of threatened species in which the United States *does not* appear? Why do you think the United States appears to be doing better with those two animal groups?

- In which category is the U.S. ranked the highest in threatened species and by a large margin? Why would the U.S. be such an unfavorable environment for the survival of these species?

- What pattern do you see emerging as you compare threatened and known species with world economic development regions?

- Which country do you believe overall has the most threatened species? Go to a map of that country using *Find Places* and read about the physical geography of the region. Then compare that to the social and economic conditions. Can you explain why this country's wildlife is so endangered?

Saving the whales and the snails is a vexing problem that combines not only environmental challenges but also involves economic development and cultural issues. Welcome to the zoo!

Keywords: environment, endangered species, economic development

Part Three

Activities for *Physical Geography* Using Encarta® Virtual Globe

Zoning in on Greenwich: Giving You the Time of Day

It's time to go to Greenwich, England, and zone in on the history and applications of time zones. Use the *Find Places* tool to create a map of Greenwich. Go to *Web Links* and select *Greenwich 2000* and click on *Time*. If you have ever had a question about time zones or what time it might in another location, this is the place to use to synchronize your watches! Select *Time FAQs* (frequently asked questions) and read about the history of time and the role of Greenwich in time zone development and you should be able to answer the following questions. What transportation innovation necessitated the creation of time zones? Why was Greenwich chosen as the center of world time keeping and what is the name of the line of longitude that passes through this British town? Astronomers in Greenwich were "dropping the ball" long before the New Year's Eve revelers in Time Square in New York City got into the act. Why did Greenwich scientists start this tradition in 1833 and why did they start dropping their "time-ball" everyday at 1:00pm? When, where, and why did the U.S. Navy get into the time-ball routine? What accounts for the differences between "UT1" and "UTC?" Why did UTC replace "GMT?" What is "atomic time" and how does it relate to the earth's rotation?

Now step back on the *Greenwich 2000* home page and click on the *Time Zones* icon on the left side of your screen. Why would the military use different time zone designations than civilians? Where would you be if you lived in the "whiskey" time zone? How about taking a trip to the "bravo" zone? What are the military and civilian time zone names for Russia (identified as "USSR")? And speaking of the former Soviet Union, let's take a side trip through numerous time zones on the Trans-Siberian Railway. Use the *Find Content* tool and enter *Trans-Siberian Railway* and click on the listing for *Sights and Sounds*. How many time zones would you travel through if you boarded the train at Moscow and ventured to the end of the line in Vladivostock? If you began your trip at 5:00am, what time would it be in Vladivostock? What time would the Omsk train station clock show at the moment of your departure from Moscow? You can verify the locations of the Russian time zones by going back to the *Greenwich 2000* Web page and clicking on *Time Zones* and select the *Map of World Times*. For a larger scale map with place locations, scroll down the page and go to the map for Russia and check your time zone calculations.

Imagine taking a similar trip but this time you are driving and departing from Francois, Newfoundland, at 2:00am on a Tuesday. Just before you leave your house you call your friend in San Francisco, California to let them know you are headed their way. What time would it be at your friend's house and which day of the week? When you locate Francois, click on *Sights and Sounds* and find out what distinction these residents enjoy every year on December 25?

If you still have time on your hands, you might want to click on the *Times Around the World* link on the *Greenwich 2000* Web page. This site defines all types of time including geologic, archaeological, chronologies, solar time, and sidereal time. You can even take a trip to Boulder, Colorado and set your watch by the "Atomic Clock" so you will never be late for class again!

Keywords: time zones, Greenwich, UTC, GMT, Russia, Trans-Siberian Railway, atomic time

(Sing along!)
There's a Hole, There's a Hole,
There's a Hole at the Bottom
of the World:
Ozone Depletion in Antarctica

Have you ever purchased sunglasses or sunscreen
lotion for the purpose of ultraviolet ray (UV)
protection? Imagine how much lotion you would
have to purchase to protect a continent! Antarctica is
a living laboratory for the study of the ozone layer,
the atmospheric shield that protects the earth from
harmful UV rays. Go to a map of the world's coldest
and driest continent to learn more about ozone (O_3)
depletion in Antarctica and its global implications.

To get vital background information on Antarctica,
click on *Geography* and read about the region's
physical, historical, and political characteristics.
What does Antarctica have in common with the
Sahara? How much of the world's fresh water is held
in cold storage on Antarctica? Who owns Antarctica
and what types of economic activities are permitted
there? While there are no permanent residents on
Antarctica, scientists comprise the largest guest
population. See how humans and animals cope with
living in this challenging environment by taking a
tour of Antarctica via *Sights and Sounds*. Many
researchers in residence are studying the condition of
the ozone layer. Why would Antarctica prove to be

such an excellent location for such analysis? For answers to this and other questions, go to *Web Links*, select *Gateway to Antarctica*, then click on *Science*. Scroll down the page and link to the *Ozone Depletion* page and follow the links to solve the following problems. Why does Antarctica lose up to 50 percent of its ozone layer in springtime? How is the ozone layer restored during the Antarctic summer? What role do chlorine and chlorofluorocarbons (CFCs) play in the destruction of the ozone layer? Why is the stability of CFCs so dangerous to ozone? What are "greenhouse gases" and what do they have in common with ozone? What are some of the more dire consequences of ozone loss? What type of radiation do both ozone and CFC's absorb and how might this be contributing to global warming?

What is a "TOMS" image and how it is used to evaluate ozone layer conditions? You can view a TOMS satellite image on this web page (Figure 1). You can also link to a TOMS site by going back to the *Ozone Depletion* home page and scroll down until you find the *TOMS Homepage*. Click on that sight and select the *Today's Ozone* icon. Find out what a Dobson Unit measures by clicking on the link by the same name. You can also calculate the thickness of the ozone layer over your own town by clicking on *Ozone Value Over Your House*. Enter the latitude and longitude coordinates for your location and a recent date and the TOMS measurement will be calculated for you. It might be helpful for you to read about how this page uses geographic grid coordinates by clicking on *Latitude and Longitude* before entering your location. You can determine your coordinates by going to a map of your hometown and using the Location Sensor tool. Compare that figure with TOMS measurements for the following locations: Christchurch, New Zealand; Bogota, Columbia; Calgary, Alberta, Canada; and Tokyo, Japan. How would you explain the differences or similarities?

In the meantime, perhaps you should put on your sunglasses and reach for some UV protection!

Keywords: ozone, ozone layer, CFCs, Antarctica, TOMS, greenhouse gases, global warming, Dobson Unit

Keeping Your Head Above Water: Sea Levels and Global Warming

Has anyone ever offered to sell you oceanfront property in Arizona? Even with the most dire predictions of sea level rise due to global warming, Phoenix residents shouldn't start worrying--yet. Many scientists believe that a general warming of the earth's temperatures and the subsequent warming and expansion of ocean waters could result in as much as a 35 inch increase in sea levels. While three extra feet of water depth may not sound like much to you, for residents of low-lying or flood-prone areas such as the Maldives or Bangaldesh, the results would be devastating. Take a trip to the island nation of the Maldives and read about the region's *Geography*. Why are the Maldives officials concerned about global warming? Click on *Sights and Sounds* and take a look at the *Coral Islands of the Maldives*. Based on what you have learned, would you be interested in buying a beach house on the Maldives in the coming years? Now conduct a similar investigation for Bangladesh. What makes this country particularly flood-prone and vulnerable to seawater incursion should sea levels experience a significant rise?

Other nations are equally concerned with global warming and the potential for rising sea levels and are taking a proactive approach in research, education, and planning. One such country is Canada. Go to a *Physical Features* map of Canada and see if you can identify coastal areas that would be at greatest risk of sea water flooding. Zoom in on the map for a closer look. Are any major cities in danger of going under water? Now switch to *Web Links* and click on *Environment Canada* which may be read in either English or French. Go to *The Green Lane* and follow the links to the headline *Climate Change--it's Real* then go to *What is Climate Change?* At the bottom of that page, click on A Matter of Degrees--A Primer on Climate Change and select section six, *The Impacts of Climate Change*. According to the information presented in this section, what are Canada's greatest concerns about global warming? What would be some of the economic impacts of global warming for the average Canadian? Which locations in Canada are believed to be at greater risk of flooding due to storm surges and sea level rises? Other than flooding, what are some other negative effects of rising saltwater? How would Canadian flora and fauna distribution and diversity be altered by increases in global average temperatures?

For additional reading, go back to the *Impact on Climate* page and follow the link to *What Can Be Done About Climate Change*. These pages illustrate how Canadian scientists and government

officials plan to approach global warming and how they hope to mitigate the negative effects of increasing temperatures. How do you as an individual contribute to the global warming process?

145

What solutions are offered on this web site to reverse the warming trend?

The "Green Lane" environmental sites are extensive and you can continue to explore the many links related to global warming, in particular those for El Niño. Now, about that oceanfront property in Calgary....

Keywords: global warming, temperature, climate, sea level rise, flooding, Maldives, Bangladesh, Canada

Somewhere Over the Rain Shadow

Some mountain ranges are so tall that they can actually block weather patterns, thus modifying the weather and climate on different sides of the mountains. In the United States, mountain ranges that are tall enough to dramatically effect the weather and rainfall patterns would include the Sierra Nevada Range in California and the Cascade Range in Oregon and Washington.

As we have learned, all of the temperate mid-latitude areas in the United States are subject to the Prevailing Westerlies (i.e., winds and weather patterns normally travel from west to east) . The sheer mass and height of these aforementioned large Western mountain ranges force aloft air masses that are moving from west to east. As these air masses rise, they cool down and condense. If conditions are right, there is considerable precipitation associated with this orographic lifting as it is called. In the wintertime this precipitation often falls in the form of snow. A large amount of snow pack in the winter and a rapid rate of melting in the spring can often determine if sites on the windward side of the mountain might be flooded.

Given the prevailing wind direction, which is the wettest side of the Cascades and Sierra Nevadas? The western slopes of the Sierras are the only place in the United States one can see the giant Sequoias and both the Sierras and Cascades contain redwood

147

trees on their western flanks. What happens to the air masses as they pass over the crest of these mountain ranges onto the eastern slopes? To find out, click on *Find* and then *Content* and search for the word *Orographic*. The paragraph therein contained explains the rain shadow effect of the warmer, drier air as it descends the eastern

flank of these mountains. Where do you think the rainfall would be greatest--in the more southerly Sierras or the more northerly Cascades? Hint: What is the temperature of the water bodies over which the air masses form that are most influential in these two disparate areas? What is the moisture holding capacity of a warm air mass vis-à-vis a cold air mass?

Now click on the sidebar marked *World Flights* and it should take you to a 3-D representation of the landscape (Western North America) as you might view it from several thousand feet up in an airplane. You can control the speed of the aircraft and the direction of the simulated flight by using the directional arrows outside the main viewing window. Experiment with stopping the plane in flight (something that is well neigh impossible on the real thing), dipping down to lower altitudes and then zooming back up to a reasonable cruising altitude. Pretend you are taking a traverse from Seattle in western Washington to Spokane in eastern Washington. How would you describe the landscape changes you see there? What are the names of the two peaks that can be viewed from Seattle? Do you think that they are volcanic in origin? Why or why not?

Now, bring up a map of the state of Washington by clicking on *Find* and the *Places* and typing in *Washington*. Using the scroll bar, request a *Comprehensive* style map. The annual precipitation in the state can vary from more than 150 inches of rain per year in the temperate rainforest of the Olympic National Park to less than 20 inches of naturally occurring rainfall in the rain shadow of the Cascades. Despite this low amount of naturally occurring rainfall, Washington's "apple valleys" (e.g., Yakima, Wenatchee) produce the famous red and yellow delicious apples that are shipped everywhere in the United States. Where does the water for these orchards come from? Click on *Sights and Sounds* and examine the slide called *Majestic Mount Rainier* and another entitled *Hoh Rain Forest*. How tall is Mount Rainier? The Hall of Mosses is in the Hoh Rain Forest in Olympic National Park. Locate the Olympic National Park and Mount Rainier on the map of Washington. Explain as effectively as you can why the National Park receives over 150 inches of rainfall a year and the eastern flank of Mount Rainier less than 20.

Keywords: orographic effect, Prevailing Westerlies, Cascades, Sierras, rain shadow

A World Wind Tour

The age of sailing vessels and exploration of
unknown territories was literally fueled by the wind.
Knowing where and when the winds would blow
meant the difference between success and failure, life
and death. It's no wonder that so many places across
the globe gained their prominence or even their
names due to their location in relationship to wind.
Let's go with the flow and explore the world by the
winds on the good ship Encarta.

We will begin our journey on Zanzibar Island.
Create a map of this Tanzanian territory and click on
Geography. How did the island gain prominence as
a trading center? What sorts of commodities were
bought and sold on Zanzibar? As you are reading
this section, click on *Trade Winds* (you might want to
print the trade winds map for future reference).
Which of the trades would effect the island? How
did the monsoon winds influence early trading
patterns? To get a true feel for the character of this
area, select *Sights and Sounds* and take in a view of
Zanzibar harbor as we sail away for the Pacific
Ocean and Australia.

As you sail around the coast of the Australian
continent you will observe a variety of environments
which are shaped by prevailing wind patterns. Select
an *Ecoregions* map of Australia. Where do you find
rainforests in Australia? Read *Land and Climate* for
more information on how the country's climate and

vegetation patterns are shaped by atmospheric circulation. When does Tasmania experience its heaviest rainfall and what winds are responsible? What is the source of the hot dry winds of Australia's interior? Travel around the coast to the Great Australian Bight and view the Nullarbor Plain via *Sights and Sounds*. How does wind work to create such a landscape? Click on *Geography* to find out how a combination of coastal characteristics and wind created havoc for sailors attempting to navigate the Bight.

Our next destinations include a series of Pacific Islands, first of which is New Caledonia. Go to *New Caledonia* and click on *Sights and Sounds* to view the coast as we approach the French territory. How do trade winds work to moderate the island's climate? Why does the northeast side of the island receive more precipitation than the lower western shore? Go to a *Comprehensive* map of New Caledonia and prepare to sail northeast toward Fiji. Take a brief landfall on Viti Levu, Fiji's largest island. How do trade winds help to create rain forests here? Now we must leave Fiji and set a northerly course for Micronesia and its capital Palikir. Palikir is located on the island of Pohnpei. Read about Palikir by selecting *Geography*. How did the capital's architects attempt to combine local culture and history along with the island's physical geography, in particular, trade winds and monsoons? Now let's move on to Hawaii. We want to visit the wettest place on earth, Wailua Falls. Bring up a map of the falls on Kauai Island and take a virtual visit via *Sights and Sounds*. Which of the trade winds brings over 400 inches of rain to the region?

From Hawaii, sail east toward South America and the coast of Ecuador and the city of Guayaquil. What is the source of the winds that work to moderate Guayaquil's climate in spite of equatorial location? Why do these winds lose their cooling effect in January? Click on *Guayaquil* and select *Geography* to read about the city and the surrounding region. How does the Humboldt Current influence Guayaquil's climate? Would this city be affected by El Niño events?

Our final stop in our world wind tour is the Caribbean. Where are the Windward and Leeward Islands? How do regional wind patterns create economic opportunities, but also hazards? In stark contrast to the islands we visited in the Pacific, Curaçao is more desert than lush tropical paradise. Take a moment to Find Curaçao and take a look at the island by clicking on *Sights and Sounds*. Check out the beaches and the island's desert countryside. Which trade winds are working to bend the divi-ivis? How are these winds different than those that influence New Caledonia?

Keywords: wind, trade winds, Pacific Ocean, Australia, Fiji, Micronesia, Ecuador, New Caledonia, Hawaii, Caribbean

Gone With the Wind

Tornadoes and hurricanes can unleash some of the most lethal damage of any natural hazard event. The winds in a tornado are so strong they can drive a straw through a telephone pole. It is almost impossible to measure their maximum speed but it is well over 300 mph. The destruction they usually leave in their wake is somewhat localized. It is rare for a tornado to cut a swath through an area more than one-half to one mile in width and they often touch down on the ground in an erratic manner. A hurricane, on the other hand, is a dangerous storm over a much larger area than a tornado. Wind speeds in the most damaging hurricanes (class 5) can approach two hundred miles per hour. The area affected by the high winds, high seas, heavy rains, and frequent flooding can extend for hundreds of miles.

Residents of a region still remember infamous hurricane names and the damage they can do. Most long-term residents of the East Coast of the United States could tell you all about either Hurricane Carol (1954) or Donna (1955) depending on which one did the most damage in their area. Likewise, Andrew (1992) will be forever vivid in the minds of south Florida residents, Hugo (1989) for the residents of the coastal Carolinas, Camille (1969) for folks who call southern Mississippi and Louisiana home and Opal (1995) for the white sand beach communities of the Florida panhandle. The fury of the hurricane starts to diminish as the weather event leaves the ocean and begins to make its way across land. Many go only a few miles inland before the energy dissipates and the hurricane is downgraded to a tropical storm. At other times, a hurricane can travel hundreds of miles inland. Charlotte, North Carolina, for example, experienced thousands of downed trees and power lines as a result of Hurricane Hugo (1989) that reached landfall between Myrtle Beach and Charleston, South Carolina, hundreds of miles away.

It is estimated that 54 percent of the population in the United States lives within 50 miles of a coastline, so a large proportion of the population could conceivably be at risk. Let's find out more about these widespread, and sometimes devastating, cyclonic storms. We'll look at some material on hurricanes in general and then focus on Hurricane Andrew (1992) that was so devastating to south Florida and southern Louisiana.

Click on *Find* and then click on *Content*. Type in *tornadoes* or *hurricane* and you will be linked to printed information on Monsoons, Tropical Storms, and Tornadoes. Read that information and answer the following questions: 1. In the Atlantic and western Pacific Oceans, a major tropical storm is called a hurricane. What are such storms called in the eastern Pacific? ...the Indian Ocean? ...colloquially in Australia? 2. What is the direction of rotation of a hurricane in the Northern Hemisphere? What is the general direction of travel of a Northern Hemisphere hurricane? 3. What force then turns them back in a northeasterly direction?

154

Let's go to a meteorological Web site that is not directly linked to Encarta, but one that contains a gold mine of valuable information. Click on *Web Links* and when you see the website address listed at the bottom of the page in Encarta, replace it with the following Website address: HYPERLINK http://wxp.atms.purdue.edu/hurricane/index.html You are now on-line to the meteorological archive at Purdue University that was specifically developed for hurricanes. Scroll down to the heading "Atlantic Hurricane Archive 1886-1996" and open that file. The first part of the file explains what criteria must be met for a tropical storm to be considered a depression or a storm or a hurricane. What pressure (measured in millibars of mercury equivalent) and what sustained wind speed does a hurricane have to maintain to be considered a Class 5 hurricane?

Let's look at the trajectory and statistics taken for one devastating hurricane--Andrew in 1992. Click on the year *1992* and you will see data listed for many different hurricanes that were recorded that year. The second storm listed is Andrew. How long did this hurricane last? What was the maximum wind speed obtained during Andrew? What was the minimum barometric pressure reading recorded during the hurricane event? Interestingly, at only one observation station did Andrew even achieve Category Five status. Where was that? To find out approximately where that was, record the coordinate location of observation 29 and go back to Encarta proper. Now click on *Tools* and then click on the pull-down menu at *Location Sensor*. This device in Encarta allows you to move the cursor (mouse) around until you are approximately at that latitude and longitude. The longitude is recorded as a negative number because it is west of Greenwich. What land mass is closest when Andrew was a Category Five hurricane?

If Andrew wasn't a Category Five hurricane for that long of a time period, how do you explain the tremendous destruction that it caused in south Florida? Until Hurricane Andrew, south Florida had avoided a major hurricane for almost a generation and many had been lulled into a sense of false security about hurricane season in the Caribbean. Note by the map of Andrew's trajectory that it also caused considerable damage in Louisiana. How did that happen? Specifically, how did the hurricane pick up in intensity between Florida and Louisiana? Is a hurricane that last for thirteen days (August 16-28, 1992) somewhat unusual? Why or why not?

Keywords: hurricane, Category Five, Hurricane Andrew, Florida, Louisiana

Köppen, Schmerpen:
How Can Botany Possibly Aid
Climatology?

Of all the climate classification systems, the one that
is still the most widely accepted is that first
developed by the Austrian plant geographer and
amateur climatologist Vladimir Köppen in 1918.
The system he developed has been considerably
modified by a succession of scientists. There has
certainly been a substantial increase in our
knowledge of climates in areas of the world that were
inaccessible and not studied by Köppen and his
contemporaries. Köppen was a geographer interested
in the ecological niches of different types of plants
and their tolerance for different combinations of
temperature and moisture conditions. He was in
search of plant species that might define the
boundary between two different climatic regimes.
These would be plants that are sensitive enough to
thrive in one type of climate, but languish in another.
One such plant was the citrus we know as the key
lime. How many of you have eaten key lime pie?
What color was it? It is was truly made of the key
lime, the color would have been a yellow-green, not
the much deeper green we associate with the limes
that are more commonly found in grocery stores
outside of south Florida. The key lime needs the
megathermal climate (A or B in the Köppen

classification system). They also need adequate moisture and a B climate (without some type of supplemental irrigation) would not provide the needed moisture. An examination of the Köppen map of world climates reveals only one location in the continental United States that has an A climate (an Aw savanna climate to be exact). Where is it? Not surprisingly, it includes the Florida Keys. Key limes. Florida Keys. Well, duh! Let's pay them a virtual visit. Click on *Find* and then *Content* and type in *Florida Keys*. Let's read about the best known of the Florida Keys--Key West. Who were two of the most important residents of the island? What was the name the Spanish gave to the island? The Spanish word for bone (hueso) may sound a little like the Spanish word for west (oeste). Do you think this is why we call it Key West today? What other cardinal direction is mentioned in regard to Key West? Why does that sentence stress the continental United States?

What is the ideal climate for the growth of corn (maize)? For a hint, look at the main Köppen classification for Iowa and Illinois. Do you find that same climate type in Europe? Much of the productive farmland in Europe is in one type of mesothermal climatic regime or another (i.e., a C climate). Alternatively, most of the cornbelt of the United States is within a microthermal climatic regime (a D climate in this case). It takes a lot of heat to grow a good crop of corn to full maturity, so why isn't corn (maize) grown in Europe to any great extent? How can a microthermal climate (i.e., the Dfa) build up more heat than its mesothermal counterpart (e.g., the Cfb)?

Because the Köppen classification is so intimately
tied with vegetative growth, the climate types may
bear more resemblance to Encarta's ecoregions than
to its climatic region types. Let's examine one
ecoregion that matches up fairly well with the
Köppen classification. The Mediterranean climate
(the Csb) matches fairly well with the Mediterranean
Woodlands ecosystem as detailed in Encarta.. Click
on *Find* and then on *World Themes*. Scroll down to
the section called *The Living World* and click on
Mediterranean Woodlands. Besides the area around
the Mediterranean Sea, where else in the world can
you find the Csb climate type? Do you notice that
they tend to be associated with areas of subtropical
high pressure on the western side of continents--
whether in southern California, central Chile,
southern Africa, or Australia. The rainfall pattern in
the Csb climatic regime is unusual--a winter
maximum. The summers in these climates tend to be
very dry and, as a result, the vegetation has had to
adapt to arid periods. According to the discussion
about the ecosystem, what is the scientific name for
the small trees with the small, hard leaves? Why is
there a need for such leaves? Fire is frequent and
actually helps to maintain this unique ecosystem by
periodically clearing out the shrub vegetation that
regenerates rather quickly. How come? What is the
difference between a fire-resistant tree (e.g., certain
species of cork trees) and a fire-dependent tree?
What is it about the garigue vegetation (i.e., the small
shrublets that grow profusely around the
Mediterranean Sea area) that protects them from
being eaten by foraging sheep and goats?

Although the vegetation in the Csb climates is similar, there are some unique species that are native to different Mediterranean environments. Can you name a tree or bush that is native to the South African Csb climate? How about the Australian Csb climate? What do we call the unique vegetative cover found in the hillsides of southern California Csb climates? Not all species that are planted in such environmentally sensitive niches will survive. Grapes and olives seem to be two crops that do well in these Csb climates. Why? From what you have learned in your wine appreciation classes, where are the great wine producing regions of the world? Does their spatial distribution bear a resemblance to the distribution of the Csb climatic type? You say you've never had a wine appreciation class and didn't even realize that your university offered one? Answer the question as best you can and peruse your non-credit course catalog.

Keywords: Köppen classification, corn belt, Mediterranean climate, micro-, meso- and macrothermal climates

Don't Take All Rocks For Granite, It's Sedimentary, My Dear Student, or I Never Metamorphic I Didn't Like.

Earth is probably the mother of all recyclers.   It starts out with igneous rocks, breaks them down and reconfigures them into sedimentary rocks. Then, through recrystalization--voilà--metamorphic rocks. And then you can melt them all down and start all over again.

You can take a magical mineral tour of the world and visit sites with all three types of rocks that have become well-known parts of landscapes. We will start our adventure by looking at igneous rocks in Northern Ireland.   Use the *Find Places* tool and create a map of Northern Ireland. Read about the region's physical characteristics by selecting *Geography*.   What types of minerals are commercially exploited in Northern Ireland? Are all three rock classifications represented in this list? Which rock type dominates? Look at the landscape by clicking on *Stepping Stones of an Irish Giant*, and *Newcastle on Dundrum Bay*, in *Sights and Sounds*. What types of rock are associated with each location?

For examples of sedimentary rocks, we don't have to venture to far from Northern Ireland. First, head south to Ireland and select *Sights and Sounds*.

Limestone plays an important role in Ireland and you can see how this chemically precipitated rock type creates some unique landscapes. Take a look at *Rock Garden of the Burren* and *Oceanside Cliffs*. What do these landscapes have in common? You can also see an example of fossil fuels as sedimentary rocks in the *Irish Peat Bog* slide. Why would the Irish exploit this resource as a domestic fuel source?

Metamorphic rocks are recycled rocks that have been recrystalized through heat and pressure. For example, metamorphosed shale becomes slate if it is compressed into dense flat plates but under different conditions it could also be changed into gneiss (pronounced 'nice'). You can view an amazing landscape formed by metamorphic processes by taking a trip to Katherine, Australia. Create a map of the location and take a look at *Katherine Gorge of Australia* via *Sights and Sounds*. What do you think is the relationship between the dominant metamorphic rock type and tourism in the area, in particular, the beaches (hint: think about how the metamorphic rock in question forms and how it might be eroded)? Another example of metamorphic rock can be found in the famous quarries of Carrara, Italy. Create a map of Carrara and click on *Sights and Sounds* and *Geography*. What type of rock is being extracted from this quarry and which famous sculptors have metamorphosed it into famous works of art?

Keywords: igneous, sedimentary, igneous, rocks, Northern Ireland, Ireland, Australia, Italy

Continental Blue Plate Special: Fetuccine Alfredro Wegener

The dynamics of plate tectonics are complex as they take into account forces that occur both below and above the earth's surface. Some aspects of the tectonic system are clearly evidenced by earthquakes and volcanoes such as the Pacific Ring of Fire. Other aspects of tectonics are less visible on the surface such as subduction, which occurs deep beneath the oceans. To learn more about the restless lithosphere, use *Find Content* and search for *plate tectonics*. When you list of choices come up, click on *Plate Tectonics, World Themes*.

As you review the plate tectonics discussion, there are several options you can take advantage of to enhance your understanding of the subject. First, take a look at the *Video* on plate tectonics. Who was responsible for developing the theory of continental drift? Do you find it odd that a meteorologist would have come up with an idea relating to lithospheric plates? Can you think of any similarities between atmospheric circulation and crustal movements that may have inspired the German scientist? What type of technological advances were needed to help support continental drift theory?

When you get to the slide for the *Chilean Andes*, click on the image and read about how plate tectonics shaped the landscape. After viewing the slide, switch to a map of the region and choose the *Tectonic Map*

Style. Which two lithospheric plates are involved in creating the rift that created these mountains? What are the most common types of earthquakes in this region--deep or shallow?

Continue reading and when you come to the slide of the *Young Himalayas*, click on that image and compare the orogenic characteristics of this location to those of the Andes. Which plates are involved in forming the Himalayas? Select *Geography* and learn more about the Himalayas. If asked to vacation on the Tethys Sea, would you pack your scuba gear or mountain climbing equipment?

Take a moment and review the plate boundaries map and then click on *Galapagos Rift*. How are the processes that formed the Galapagos Rift different from those which created the Himalayas? Which plates are involved in the Galapagos? What types of unique environmental conditions were created as a result of the rift formation?

Finally, click on the box for *Equitorial Megashear*. What exactly is an equitorial megashear--a really bad hair cut in Brazil? Click on each of the four megashear locations highlighted in the text. Which of these is associated with an inhabited island?

Keywords: plate tectonics, continental drift, Alfred Wegener, Andes, Himalayas, rifts, earthquakes

Return to Cinder

Everyone seems to enjoy the fireworks on the Fourth
of July. The more awe-inspiring the pyrotechnic
display the better. Likewise with volcanoes. The
best ones are seemingly those that spew forth hot,
molten lava high into the air and then spill over the
sides of the mountain that is actively being created.
The molten hot lava flows then set off forest fires and
may even threaten human life and property. Part of
why we know so much about everyday life during
the Roman Empire is that the city of Pompeii was
wiped out very quickly by the eruption of Mount
Vesuvius near present-day Naples. The population
of that city was incinerated and bodies as well as
archaeological artifacts were buried under tons of ash
and debris. We can even tell by popular phrases
written into walls around public buildings that the
residents of this Roman Empire town wrote graffiti as
forms of political and social protest.

Many people were, then, actually a bit disappointed
when, in May of 1980, Mount St. Helen's, a
stratovolcano, erupted in a thick cloud of smoke and
ash rather than in a flash of fire and light. The
mountain had been giving signals to vulcanologists
for weeks proceeding the eruption and they, in turn,
tried to warn the residents of the small towns
surrounding the mountain of the imminent danger

they faced if they chose to stay. The media turned its
attention to Mr. Harry Truman, a colorful eighty-

year-old lifelong resident of the area who was only distantly related to the former President. Mr. Truman simply refused to move; the Cascades were the only home that he ever knew. The media were saddened when debris from the violent explosion of the northern portion of the volcanic cone destroyed everything in its path, including Mr. Truman and his cabin. Let's see what we can learn about volcanoes from the Encarta material. First click on *Find* and then please click on *World Themes*. There you will find a lot of interesting material about volcanoes. Take a few minutes to examine the Video that accompanies the material. Go ahead. You know you want to!

Even if you had no sound to accompany the images, why do you think the video ends with a peasant farmer working the agriculturally rich but labor intensive terraced fields (most probably in southeast Asia)? Let's assume that the peasant farmer is working a rice field that was once formed by a lava flow. What kinds of soil form from lava flows that have undergone decomposition in tropical areas such as those shown in the video clip? Volcanic soils are very rich in nutrients and, in tropical rainforest regions where the environment is never dormant, a mature profile of soil can form from a fresh lava flow in less that 100 years. By the same token, a lava flow in Iceland may decompose less than one-quarter inch in that same time period. Soil formation takes moisture and high temperature in abundance.

Now, read the material on Volcanoes under *World Themes*. Which are more violent when they explode--volcanoes with less gaseous and more fluid magma or volcanoes with more gaseous and less fluid magma? Why do think that is? How is lava defined? How does lava affect the volcano's size and height? What are pyroclastic materials? The year after Krakatau in Indonesia exploded with such violence that it destroyed the island it was located on (1883), was known worldwide as the "year without a summer". Based on what you have read can you venture a guess as to why this was so?

Iceland suffers flooding when volcanoes erupt near glaciers. What are these floods called there? Besides Mt. St. Helen's discussed above, give two examples of stratovolcanoes. What are such volcanoes famous for?

In addition to stratovolcanoes, there are also cinder cones and shield volcanoes. Can you explain the differences among these three types? Mauna Kea in Hawaii is one of the largest shield volcanoes in the world. What is the diameter of its base? Crater Lake in Oregon is called a caldera. What is that exactly? Can you name two famous plateaus which were formed by lava flowing outward through cracks and fissures in the volcano rather than out the steam vent?

About how many volcanoes in the world are considered active? Ironically, Mount St. Helens (1980) and Mount Pinatubo (1991) in the Philippines are classified as dormant volcanoes. What famous landmark in Scotland sits atop an extinct volcano?

Keywords: volcano, Mount St. Helens, magma, lava, pyroclastic material, caldera

Permafrosting on the Cake: Weathering in Arctic Regions

Much of the northern half of Canada lies within a permafrost zone. The freeze and thaw cycles associated with this climate region work to create unique arctic landscapes with such features as pingoes, stone rings, and patterned ground. Permafrost also creates difficulties when humans attempt to establish permanent settlements. Careful planning and engineering must be implemented when constructing buildings and infrastructure in permafrost areas in order to avoid damage to foundations and underground pipes. With an extremely short growing season, traditional agricultural activities other than animal herding are virtually impossible in permafrost regions. Few large settlements are found north of the zone of continuous permafrost.

Observe this for yourself by creating an Ecoregions map of Canada. Pay close attention to the southern extent of the Boreal Ecoregion. Use the *Location Sensor* tool to determine the general latitudinal location of the boundary between Boreal and Tundra environments. Now switch to *Comprehensive map of Canada*. At this scale, how many cities do you find north of that boundary? Which of these cities has the largest population? How do those populations compare to those of cities like Edmonton, Winnipeg, or Halifax? What physical processes are at work to create tundra landscapes?

To appreciate the dramatic effects of physical weathering in permafrost regions, take a trip to the Mackenzie Mountains in Canada's Northwest Territories. Create a map of the area using the *Find Places* tool then select *Sights and Sounds* for a look at the Mackenzie Mountains. Were you surprised by the summer temperature extremes? Why are the Mackenzie Mountains so dry? How does soil moisture affect physical weathering? What types of surface features have resulted from the permafrost conditions?

The power of ice to fracture rocks, and gravity to move materials downslope are evident in the Mackenzie Mountains. You can see another example of this type of weathering by stepping back to a map of the Northwest Territories and selecting *Arctic Moraine on Baffin Island* in *Sights and Sounds*. Now go to *Geography* and read more details about the physical characteristics of the Northwest Territories. How does the combination of flat plains and rugged mountains in a permafrost region combine to promote poor drainage in the Mackenzie Valley?

You can read more about tundra and permafrost by selecting the World Themes topic, *Tundra, Polar Deserts, and Ice*.

Keywords: permafrost, tundra, physical weathering, Northwest Territories, Canada

'Mites Go Up,'Tites Come Down: Karst Sinkholes and Caves

Do you remember the incredible photograph of the Winter Park, Florida sinkhole that almost literally swallowed the exotic car dealership? The sight of Jaguars and BMWs disappearing into the ever-widening hole was almost too much to bear for a car buff! But what is a sinkhole exactly and why do they collapse and/or expand in size on occasion? Click on *Find* and then *Content* and type in *sinkhole* (all one word). How are sinkholes related to caves? What is the material from which these caves form? Are all caves everywhere made of this material? The underground caves that can run for miles and miles are normally formed from water flowing over limestone (calcium carbonate). These landscapes are called karst topographies. What are some distinguishing characteristics of a karst landscape? If we were to examine a topographic sheet for western Kentucky, portions of the Yucatan Peninsula, southeastern New Mexico, or the Dalmatian coast of Croatia we would see an absence of surface streams and some hanchured areas denoting sinkholes. In such environments many of the rivers have literally gone underground having worked their ways down through the porous and soluble limestone formations. How extensive are some of these cavern systems? Click on *Find* and then *Places* and type in *Mammoth Cave*. The cave, part of the National Park System, is appropriately named. If all of Mammoth's Cave's known underground rivers and caves were added

170

together, the total length would equal 348 miles, making it the most extensive cave system in the world. Only a few miles of the cave are actually open to the public and those areas are well lighted, well ventilated and equipped with hand rails and caution signs when the overhead clearance becomes problematic. Unless the guest is an expert spelunker who has made prior arrangements to go to parts of the cave not normally open to the public, traffic within the cave is confined to a few well-known tours. Such was not always the case. Click on *Web Links* on the sidebar and then click on the official Internet Web page for Mammoth Cave National Park. One of the recent additions to the home page is a descriptimn of a cave tour in 1844 when one Dr. Croghan owned the cave (from 1838-1849). Dr. Croghan's historic entrance is pointed out on present-day tours of the cave but is no longer used as the main way to descend into the cave. How did the visitors see into the darkness of the cave? Would such an illumination system be allowed today?

On the way to the entrance, the guests passed "the ruins of saltpeter furnaces and large mounds of ashes". What was the saltpeter used for? Why did processing of this material start up again at this location during the Civil War? In the Main Cavern itself were the ruins of hoppers or vats where "nitrous earth" was leached. What were the miners doing in this process?

How were names (and early graffiti) left on the ceiling of the Register Room? What reminded the visitors of the Gothic cathedrals of Europe? How do these natural features form? What do guests

171

normally do when they reach the Devil's Arm-Chair? How long does it take for a cave to form features such as the Cooling Tub or Napoleon's Dome?

When the party goes back to the Grand Gallery, it passes a row of cabins "built for consumptive patients". What do we call this disease today? Do you think that a cave environment where the temperature is always a constant 56 degrees Fahrenheit and the air is always a bit moist because of the water coursing through it is a good location for such a sanitarium? Why or why not?

What was on the ceiling of the Star Chamber that reminded the visitor of the "firmament itself"? How did visitors get across the "frightful chasm" (20 feet wide and 200 feet deep) of the formation known at the "Bottomless Pit"? What was the (non-politically correct) name given to the zigzag formation known as the Winding Way? Does the anecdote told by the narrator of this tour (and the accompanying lithograph) justify its more commonly used name? What names of cave features might fill the visitor with a sense of foreboding and death? What worries the guide about the Echo River in the cave that causes him to stop the boat trip after only three-quarters of a mile? What is the "dome of domes" called? What adorns the top of the formation?

Keywords: karst topography, sinkhole, Mammoth Cave, Kentucky, stalagmites, stalactites

Wet and Wild Waterfalls

Some of the most majestic features associated with streams are waterfalls. Breathtaking and beautiful, waterfalls are dramatic elements of many landscapes. Take a tour of some of the world's most fascinating waterfalls using *Sights and Sounds*. Using the *Find Content* tool, search for "waterfalls" on Encarta. Keep the list open for future reference by clicking on the "check" in the lower left corner of the *Find* window. Select the following examples from *Sights and Sounds* and begin your explorations of waterfalls.

Rio Grande Waterfall
The waterfalls on the Rio Grande of Brazil are not the world's largest but their setting within the montane cloud forest is nonetheless awe-inspiring. Would you expect to find such features associated with the Rio Grande along the U.S.-Mexican border? Why or why not?

Waterfall in the Costa Rican Highland
How does this waterfall compare to that of the Rio Grande? How do you think volcanoes effect fluvial processes in the region? Compare this slide to "Scenic Waterfall" in Iceland. What do they have in common and why are they different?

Angel Falls in Canaima National Park
The highest waterfall in the world, Angel Falls is no place for a daredevil to try his or her luck going over

in a barrel. Why are the best views of this waterfall enjoyed from above rather than from below?

Contrasts of Yosemite and Yosemite Falls
From the tallest to the world to the tallest waterfall in North America, we find ourselves at Yosemite. What geomorphic processes were at work to create these falls? How does this contrast to the falls in South America?

Island of Springs
Waterfalls in Jamaica are unique not only in their beauty but also in their economic function. How has Jamaica capitalized on waterfalls as part of their tourism economy? Compare this to the way Madagascar exploits some of their waterfalls on the slides for *Lac Alaotra*. Why would Madagascar develop such projects?

Kaieteur Falls
Based on this image, you could say that Guyana comes by its name quite honestly. What do these falls have in common with the previous waterfalls?

Icelandic Water Power
Iceland's waterfalls could provide this fossil fuel-poor country with an abundant supply of renewable energy but what might prevent that from happening?

Towering Auyan Tupay
How does this waterfall compare to others in South America?

Erawan National Park
Waterfalls can be studied as part of the physical as well as the cultural landscape. Why are these falls a good example of how natural features become entwined in local culture.

Keywords: waterfalls, fluvial processes, rainforests, hydropower, tourism

That Canyon, Steve--It's a Butte!

If you travel to many of America's state and national
parks, you know that a visit to one of these areas is
like a vacation and a physical geography field trip
wrapped into one.   Those interested in exploring a
wide variety of landform features and rock structures,
would be well-advised to head for the Rocky
Mountain region, in particular, the Colorado Plateau.

Using the *Find Places* tool, create a *Physical
Features* map of the Colorado Plateau.   The plateau
is situated in the "Four Corners" area where Arizona,
Colorado, New Mexico, and Utah come together.
Take a moment to examine the landscape. What type
of stream drainage pattern do you find in the region?
Which major rivers have their headwaters forming
within the Colorado Plateau? Zoom in on the San
Juan River. With this closer look, can you explain
the number and pattern of intermittent streams?

Now go back to a map of the Colorado Plateau and
select *Geography*.   You can take a self-guided tour
of seven national parks in the region by clicking on
the highlighted text in *Geography* and following the
links and options at each location.   After visiting
each park, go back to the *Colorado Plateau
Geography* box for your next destination.

Arches National Park
Start your tour in Utah in Arches National Park and go to the *Arches National Park* Web page. What is the dominant rock type that was sculpted to create these dramatic landscapes?

Bryce Canyon
Take a look at Bryce Canyon from a spectacular vantage point by selecting *Sights and Sounds*. How did Bryce Canyon form and how was that different from most other canyons. Go to *Web Links* and select *Formation of Bryce Canyon*. How did Native Americans interpret the origins of the canyon? What is a "hoodoo" and how does it form?

Canyonlands
Go to Canyonlands and tour the area via the *Guide to Canyonlands* Web page. What are the unique characteristics of the "Maze, Needles, and Island in the Sky?" Why is this one of the least visited parks in the region?

Capitol Reef National Park
What? A "reef" in the middle of the Colorado Plateau? And what does this park have in common with Washington, DC? What did Mormon settlers leave behind as part of the landscape? You can answer these questions by going to *Web Links* and clicking on the *Guide to Capitol Reef* page.

Grand Canyon National Park
Try looking at the grandest of all canyons from a different perspective using the *World Flights* option. Not only will you tour the Grand Canyon but you will also have an opportunity to see how surrounding

regional features. You can also select *Geography* and *Sights and Sounds* for more information and views of the Grand Canyon. What evidence exists to suggest that the canyon was once covered by a body of water?

Mesa Verde National Park
Find out how Mesa Verde earned its name by reading about the park by clicking on *Geography*. Who were the cliff dwellers who lived in the canyon and why did they live there?

Petrified Forest
Don't be afraid to visit this national park. The only things that are petrified are the fossilized trees! Read about the park by selecting *Geography*. Switch to *Web Links* and click on *Great Outdoors Recreation Pages--Petrified Forest National Park*. How did the mineral content of sediment facilitate the petrification of fallen trees? How is erosion continuing to play a key role in the development of this region?

Keywords: landforms, drainage patterns, canyons, national parks, Native Americans

Loess is More

No, we haven't switched from physical geography to
the minimalist architecture of Mies van der Rohe. We
are talking about the seemingly mundane subject of
dust. Not the dust bunnies under your bed, but rather
wind-blown dust that can build to incredible depths
in places like the steppes of the Ukraine, the plains of
the Corn Belt, or the Pampas of Argentina.

It is similar to the Dust Bowl of the 1930s in the
Great Plains of the United States? Well, yes, sort of,
except this wind-blown period lasted for eons. It
may seem ironic that there was actually a protracted
period of drought during the Ice Age. With the
presence of water in the form of ice more than a mile
thick, it is easy to forget the basic physical principle
we have learned about air masses: cold air can hold
less moisture than warm air.

What is the driest continent on the planet? It is not
Australia as often assumed. The Great Sandy Desert
(the Outback) of Australia is certainly a major
ecological component of the country/continent at
least as measured by its areal extent. A very small
proportion of the population chooses, however, to
live in this rather inhospitable environment opting
instead for the Mediterranean and subtropical
environments along the coasts. Over eighty percent
of Australia's population lives within 50 miles of the
coast.

No, the driest continent is Antarctica. All that fresh
water locked up in the form of ice has built up over
the eons. What little precipitation there is in any
given year simply adds to the ice pack. There is very
little melting because of the cold temperatures.
During the Pleistocene, wind and water in the form
of glaciers worked together to produce loess, some of
the finest and most easily worked soils in the world.
The rivulets the flowed from underneath the melting
glaciers carried the finest particles of silt that had
been sorted and sized by the processes of overland
flow and gravity. Ironically, like the continent of
Antarctica, the land area not covered by the glacier's
ice was quite dry and thus vulnerable to wind action.
The wind could easily pick up these fine silt particles
and deposit them, sometimes to remarkable depths.
Loess or wind-blown (eolian) dust is inherently
unstable and easily erodable but it is also very fertile
and easily worked by crude implements.

If you turn to Encarta and click on *Find* and then
Content and type in *loess*, you will discover that the
majority of the references are to places in China.
Sure, Belgium, Nebraska, and the Pampas are also
mentioned, but one is struck with how important
loess deposits must be to China's development by the
number of times loess is mentioned specifically in the
narrative. In the loosely packed loess of Huangtu
Gaoyuan, what do farmers do to overcome erosion?
What is the claim to fame of Huabei Pingyan?
Where is this lowland area located? In which
province? South of what major river?
What is the problem with the semi-arid loess-covered
plateau of northern Shaanxi (or Shensi) province?
Where within this province is it said that Chinese

civilization originated? What type of soil is present in the Wei He valley? What river, subject to periodic flooding, would deposit fresh alluvial sediments on this low-lying land? How many years ago were Chinese people cultivating this land?

What influence do the Qin Ling mountains have in the decision as to what crop is grown north of the range vis-à-vis what is grown to its south? What is the tallest peak in the Qin Ling range? Is that tall enough to cause an orographic effect on precipitation? If China is, for the most part, in the middle latitudes of the northern hemisphere under the predominant influence of the Prevailing Westerlies, how can an east-west trending mountain range like the Qin Ling have an effect on the weather? Is there an influence on air masses over China that we don't have in the United States? What is it?

It appears that if loess is located in a semi-arid region of China, wheat can be grown not unlike the productive Palouse Hills of Washington in the United States. If loess is located in a more well-watered, humid region of China, what is usually grown? Can you name some areas of China that might be supported by loess soils? What about the Henan province with its dense population of 80 million persons? What role do you think the "fertile loess uplands" of the province's central area play in the agricultural production of the province and its ability to support that many people?

Keywords: loess, China, Huang He River, Shaanxi Province, Henan Province, Huabei Pingyan, Huangtu Gaoyuan

The Iceman Misseth: Implications for the Driftless Area

Examine any map of the advance of the most recent continental glacier (Laurentide Ice Sheet). You might notice that the glaciers stopped at the Missouri and Ohio Rivers. But, a feature that is less noticeable is that the most recent continental glaciation missed an area of southwestern Wisconsin, northeastern Iowa, and northwestern Illinois. Glacial specialists speculate that the glacier broke into two lobes and that the so-called Driftless Area was simply spared the most recent glacial advance. What implications does having a glacier miss a reasonably large chunk of real estate have for the underlying topography and landscape in this region vis-à-vis some of the nearby areas of those same states that were more recently glaciated? Click onto *Find* and then *Content* and type in *Driftless AND Area*. In what state is the term Driftless Area actually used? The same idea (although not alluded to by name) is discussed in the description of Wisconsin. What appears to be the most important tourist location within the Driftless Area of Wisconsin? Of what easily erodable material are the formations of the Wisconsin Dells composed? Judging from its location, what force do you think did the eroding? What does the word Dells mean? Does it have the same meaning as The Dalles in the state of Oregon? According to the brief description of the Wisconsin Dells, what was the name of city before 1931? See if you can spot Spring Green, Wisconsin on the map. It is also in the driftless area and a place with such delightful vistas that famed architect Frank Lloyd Wright opened a design studio there called Taliesin. One of his students built a house nearby out of all natural materials on a limestone outcrop of the Wisconsin River. Now called the House on the Rock, it too is a major tourist attraction.

Within the driftless region of northeastern Illinois is the town of Galena. To find out more about Galena, click on *Find* and then *Places* and type in *Iowa*. When there, go to *Web Links* and open *Iowa Tourism*. Within *Tourist Regions*, click on *East Iowa* and, surprisingly perhaps, you will find a site for Galena, Illinois located right across the Mississippi River from Iowa. Now link with the site called *Jim Post's Galena*. What does the word galena mean? What metal is made from galena ore? Why would that metal be important to the war effort during the Civil War? What U.S. President is most closely associated with Galena, Illinois (hint: some of his initials are contained in this sentence but he's not buried in a tomb in Galena but rather in New York City)?

In Iowa, the driftless area has the greatest local relief in the entire state. The name the citizens of Iowa have bestowed upon the state's highest point is Pike's Peak. Can you find it on the map of Iowa? It may be difficult to spot precisely. It is more than 900 feet tall. One town with an interesting history in the driftless region of Iowa is Decorah. Can you locate it on the map of Iowa? The locals call this part of the state "Little Switzerland" (We told you they had an ironic sense of humor). But, where did the bulk of the residents of Decorah come from? Click on the *Web Link* for *Iowa Tourism* and then on *Tourist Regions* and *Northeast Iowa*. Would it help to know that Decorah is the home of Luther College? The home of the Norwegian-American Heritage Museum? Decorah is a place where rosemauling is an important artform to be preserved. What is rosemauling? What is the name of the port city in Europe from which the forebears of most Decorah residents left the old country?

Further east along the bluffs of the Mississippi River is the regional capital of this part of the state- Dubuque, Iowa. What is unusual about this city? The French explorers Jacques Marquette and Louis Joliet founded it. Many of the residents are of French heritage. There are two Catholic colleges, a Trappist monastery and the highest proportion of Roman Catholic adherents of any city in the United States outside of south Texas.

But what about the physical features of Dubuque? Note that one tourist attraction, called the Fenelon Place Cable Car Elevator, that claims to be the shortest, steepest railroad in the United States. Why do you think a city like Dubuque needs an elevated (inclined) railway?

Keywords: driftless area, glaciation, Wisconsin Dells, WI, Dubuque, IA, Galena, IL

Our Just Deserts: Soil Erosion

If there is one resource we take for granted it would
probably be soil. Most of us do not realize that
while it can take millions of years for soils to form,
soils can be destroyed in a matter of minutes. While
erosion and deposition are both part of the natural
soil forming process, human intervention can
accelerate both with disastrous consequences. Soil
erosion is one of the most important environmental
issues facing us now and into the next century. Let's
look at some of the issues associated with soil
erosion.

Using the *Find World Themes* menu, select *Soil
Erosion and Exhaustion*. Read the first section on
Soil and Food then click on the slide for
Deforestation in Madagascar. How has
deforestation in Madagascar resulted in soil erosion?
Why will it be difficult to reverse this trend and
implement soil preservation programs?

Lake Turkana is another example of how soil erosion
is creating a serious environmental crisis in Africa.
Click on the slide for *Lake Turkana*. What
differences can you detect between the two satellite
images? What type of agriculture is increasing
siltation in Lake Turkana? Where is this soil coming
from? Read *The Causes of Soil Erosion and
Exhaustion* for more information on how agricultural
production effects soil. Do you think we have
learned our lessons about soil erosion since the Dust

Bowl days? To find out, use the *Find World Themes* index once more and select *Desertification*.

The spread of deserts usually results in the loss of productive soils. Farmland can be buried underneath blowing silt and sand. Once soils have been degraded in this way, it is very difficult and expensive to reverse the process. Where climates are dry and irrigation is utilized to increase production, soil can be degraded by salinization. Take a look a the slide titled *Encroachment*. Would you want to produce food for your family on this land? Find out more by reading *Geography of Desertification*. Where are deserts expanding at the expense of arable land? How can you explain desertification in Siberia or Alaska and how are these situations different from those experienced in the Sahel of Africa?

As you read through the "Devegetation" section, what can you conclude about the relationship between livestock raising and soil erosion? How does this fit in with deforestation? What would be your argument against clearing rainforests for the sake of grazing cattle? How will we be able to increase food production without clearing more land? Is it possible to reclaim soil that has been polluted, degraded, or has simply gone with wind?

Keywords: soil, erosion, desertification, agriculture, Africa, deforestation, irrigation

Act Locally, Think Globally

At last we come to the final activity related to the
physical textbooks and, for the first time in awhile,
the title to this exercise isn't particularly funny. In
fact, it's a saying you may have seen on a bumper
sticker. You may even have it on your own vehicle.
If so, good for you! Sometimes the Earth's
environmental problems including global warming,
acid rain, and ozone depletion seem so bleak and so
much beyond the scope of an individual to do much
about, that it is easy to accept a defeatist or fatalistic
attitude.

Let's see what Encarta has to say about some of the
world's environmental problems. Click on *Learn
about the Earth* and then scroll down to the section
entitled *Environmental Challenges*. There are
several interesting ones to choose from, but one that
has been directly linked to the increase in greenhouse
gases (such as carbon dioxide in the atmosphere) is
the burning and deforestation, especially in the
tropical rainforests. So, click on *Deforestation* and
listen to the accompanying Video Clip. The problem
of deforestation goes beyond the tropical rainforests
of South America, Africa, and southeast Asia. All
forests everywhere appear to be under threat.

Besides the obvious loss of trees (and the very long
period of time that it takes for a forest to regenerate

in many temperate to subarctic environmental niches), what are some other environmental problems exacerbated or directly caused by deforestation? That material in Encarta suggests that tropical deciduous forests are in "worse straits" than their wet tropics counterparts. Why is this? In a tropical rainforest, where are most of the nutrients and soluble minerals held? What is slash-and-burn agriculture (a.k.a. swidden or milpa agriculture)? As currently practiced, why does it provide only a temporary boost to the fertility of tropical soils?

As we focus on deforestation, click on *Web Links* on the sidebar that takes you to some World scale Web sites. Scroll until you find the *World Wildlife Federation Global Network* site and open it. You'll see their symbol--that cute but endangered giant Panda. Click on the bar marked *Forests for Life*. What percentage of the world's forests is currently unprotected (i.e., not within a national park or national forest or some protected reserve)? Since we said that we should Act Locally (and perhaps Globally as well), let's click on the button marked *Act Now*. And since we are really going to be proactive when we get to the next screen, let's click on *Take Action*. What is the "hot button issue" of concern? When this exercise was developed it was concerned about deforestation of one of the last remaining native (i.e., old growth and never logged) lowland temperate forests in Europe.

Since Europe is relatively small and very densely populated overall, it may seem to you like a miracle that any native forest remains. This stand of timber is called the Bialowieza Primeval Forest. What does the term "primeval" mean? Where is this forest stand located? Is the fact that it straddles an international boundary a complicating factor in the preservation of its pristine state? Of the 550 square kilometers on the Polish side of Bialowieza, how much was set aside by the Polish government as protected (national park)? What lending agency of international renown has been cast in the role of villain in this particular case? How often do you think that international lending agencies and international environmental groups are at loggerheads over the preservation of the natural environment?

OK. So we want to act locally. What does the World Wildlife Fund suggest we do? Click on the the man in the chair with the question mark over his head. That icon is called *What Can I Do Anyway?*. Besides educating yourself on environmental issues of pressing concern around the world (such as the destruction of the entire Bialowieza Primeval Forest in three to five years under current rates of forest product extraction), what else can you do?

The site suggests e-mailing officials in Poland demanding (in a polite way of course) that the moratorium on logging be continued and that the Polish portion of the primeval forest be set aside as national park. Out of curiosity, why do you think the World Wildlife Fund has not urged the same sort of e-mail campaign for officials in Belarus, the country that contains the remainder of this primeval forest?

Keywords: Environment, Deforestation, Poland, Wet Tropics, Lowland Temperate Forests, Environmental Action

Part Four

Activities for *Economic Geography* Using Encarta® Virtual Globe

One Picture Tells a Thousand Geographies (or Where's Wheeler?)

How often have you spent even a nanosecond of your time studying the cover of a textbook? Okay, so sometimes you don't even want to look at what's inside, but just this once, take a few minutes and examine the cover photo on you Economic Geography text. What do you see--aside from the title, edition number, and authors' names? If you had to write a story to go with this image, what would it be? Where do you think this photo was taken and what is its geographic message? Using a little detective work, find physical, cultural, and economic evidence to help identify the country depicted in the cover photo.

Where should you start your story? First, let's focus our attention on narrowing down the locational possibilities. To do this, start with the clues offered by the physical landscape. Using the *Map Styles* tool, select *Natural*, then *Ecoregions* map types. You should now have a map of global environments on the screen. Check the symbolization by selecting the sidebar titled *About This Map*. Make your decision as to which region you would like to zoom in on. Based on the ecoregion type you believe is represented in the photo, zoom in to take a closer look. Compare the soil and vegetation on the map to those in the cover photo until satisfied you are in the correct region. Click on *Land and Climate* for additional environmental information. If you believe you're in the right area, move on to the cultural clues.

Examine the cultural landscape depicted in the photo. What can you tell from the people in the foreground? What they wearing? Perhaps there are some ethnicity or religion clues in the photo? Look at the architecture. Is there anything that would help you identify the location? For some help, check out *Sights & Sounds* and *Society* selections. If you don't see anything that looks like it matches with the cover photo, perhaps you should select a different region.

Now let's get down to business. What do you think about the economic landscape portrayed in the cover photo? Is this a highly urbanized country? What are the employment characteristics? Is this a high tech region? Do you find the satellite dish incongruous with the landscape? What sort of quality of life might the people in the foreground expect to experience? Go to *Statistics* for the country you have selected to see if your interpretations are correct.

You've investigated, now it's decision time. You may not have the exact location but you should be in at least the correct region or country. What do you think? Where was the photo taken and what is your cover story?

Keywords: Economic Geography, Ecoregions, Cultural Landscape

Painting the World By Numbers

It may come as no surprise that the table on page 20
in your text lists China as the country with the
world's largest population. What you may not
realize is that the rate of population change for China
is less than some other countries on the list. To
better understand the world population issue, it's
important to compare and contrast demographic
characteristics. Let's rearrange this table by ranking
countries by other statistics we can find using
Encarta.

Using Table 2.1 from your text, "Leading Countries
in Population," create another table using *Statistics*
(*Population and Health & Education*). You can do
this on a piece of graph paper or on a spreadsheet.
Sort the data by the countries listed for:

> Birth Rates
> Death Rates
> Fertility Rates
> Population Density
> Population Growth Rates
> Population Rural
> Calorie Supply
> Infant Mortality Rates
> Literacy Rates

How does China compare to other countries in light of these other statistics? In your opinion, which countries on your list face the most serious population problems?

Now consider this. All of these statistics are averages and averages can be misleading. For example, imagine you go rabbit hunting. Up jumps a bunny and you shoot with your double-barreled shotgun. Boom! You miss to the right. Boom! You miss to the left. On average, you hit your target right between the eyes. Or did you? The key to interpreting certain statistics is recognizing that they often fail to show the distribution of phenomena but rather only the average of two extremes. Population density is an excellent example of this. One problem with this statistic is that it is often used to interpret standards of living rather than what it really measures--the numbers of persons per square unit of area. The assumption is frequently made that high population densities often translate into low qualities of life. Does the country listed at the top of the table with the highest population density have a low standard of living? Check out the population density for the United States. Bring up a map of the United States. Under *Map Styles*, select *Human*, then *Population*. How many places are actually close to the population density listed in the *Statistics* table for the entire U.S.? Where do you find the highest and lowest population densities in the United States and how do those numbers compare with standards of living within those regions or states?

Try your own hand at matching up statistics. The numbers can be misleading and instructive all at the same time.

Happy data hunting!

Keywords: Population, Demographics, Standard of Living, Statistics, Population Density

Thumbs Down: A Hitchhiker's Guide to the Globe

If you reside in an industrialized country, you probably take certain things for granted. You might expect to own more than one car (or might already do so!). If you live in the United States, you may enjoy the convenience of accessible personal transportation and also many communications options such as telephones, cable television, and the Internet. Imagine how difficult it would be to get through your day without electricity, running water, telephone, paved highways, or for some, even cable television. We can look at economic development through these consumer conveniences to get a feel for how the majority of the world--the have nots--live. For example, Tables 3.2 and 3.3 in your text illustrate that the flow of information may be difficult in some world regions simply by the lack of telephones or published materials.

Modern transportation is essential in fostering economic development and the flow of goods, people, and information. Not everyone has adequate transportation access. Let's look at some locations where motorized transportation is limited and how this reflects broader development issues. Or, where hitchhikers might be waiting quite some time for a ride.

First, we need a thematic map based on numbers of passenger vehicles. Select *Map Styles* then *Statistical*. Create a world map of passenger vehicles and identify the regions with the lowest and highest available personal transportation. What pattern does this reveal? What are the ten countries with the lowest numbers of passenger vehicles? What else do these countries have in common? If motor vehicles are hard to find, how do people, goods, and information travel in these areas? How does this effect economic development? What types of alternative transportation are used if motor vehicles are not available? Can you think of any advantages to using animals for transportation rather than machines? Let's travel to some locations where this makes perfect sense. First, go to Thailand and select *Sights and Sounds*. Check out the slide for *Domesticated Working Animals*. Next, head for Greece and take a look at the *Threshing Wheat* and *Herding Sheep* slides in *Sights and Sounds*. Why would Greek farmers choose draft animals for these activities? Wander up to Azerbaijan and look at the horse farm in *Sights and Sounds* or to Ukraine and see how draught horses are used. Create a map of Nepal and select *Sights and Sounds*. Click on *Precarious Footpaths*. Would you want to drive a car along that road? And what types of "beasts of burden" are transporting commodities in the *Isolated Mountain People* slide? Finally, let's visit Ethiopia and read about its *Infrastructure* by clicking on *Society*. Perhaps the *Horse-Drawn Taxi* picture in Ethiopia is the best example of how even urban transportation isn't always motor-driven. Go to the *Ethiopia--A Country Study Web Link* and select *Transportation and Communications*. How many miles of "all-weather roads" are there in Ethiopia? How does route density compare to other African nations and how does this affect the lives of the average rural dweller in Ethiopia?

Certainly a lack of modern transportation and communications systems inhibits economic development. But can you think of any advantages to using livestock over motor vehicles for transportation and work? Think about this. Draft animals can reproduce themselves, provide fertilizer, are less likely to overturn on steep slopes, require less technology, and do less damage to soil structure than tractors. They can also be fed with crops and plants found nearby. Where would you fill up your tank in rural Ethiopia or have an engine overhauled? How long would you wait for spare parts in Ukraine or Azerbaijan? Does a yak ever need a front-end alignment? And that's no yoke!

Keywords: transportation, infrastructure, motor vehicles, draft animals

Banking on Technology

It's relatively easy to see the relationships between urbanization and the size and influence of financial centers such as the influence of Tokyo as the world's largest metropolitan and banking center. But what of countries and cities outside the industrialized realm-- how do they acquire the financial resources needed for development? Think of yourself as a citizen of a developing country with a per capita income of less than $1000 per year. How would you afford a college education for yourself or your children? Could you go to a bank and get a loan to buy a new tractor or to acquire more land to farm if you told the lending officer that you make less than $100 per month?

One approach taken by countries outside of the industrialized realm is to work together to overcome their lack of investment capital and technology. Some of these countries have been so far behind the technology and communications curve it would have been impossible for them to ever catch up without a cooperative effort. An excellent example of this scenario is the Group of 15 (G-15), the leading members of the Non-Aligned Movement (NAM). The fifteen member countries work together to share technology and economic data and promote trade and economic development among the members countries. To learn more about this innovative approach, click on *Find Content* and enter *Group of 15* to read more about this alliance in the *Glossary*.

Take a moment and examine the list of countries that belong to the G-15. If the goal of this group is to foster "south-south" trade, what sort of goods or services do you think might be exchanged between any pair of these countries? Also, some of these countries are arguably better-off in some development categories than others. For example, you might not immediately think of Mexico as being in the same category as Senegal or Peru having much in common with India.

To gain a better understanding of why these countries chose to align themselves, you can compare imports and exports as well as their major trading partners by using *Find Country* and selecting *Facts and Figures* for each member nation. See if any countries exhibit trade complementarity. Also, you can make a quick comparison of their economies and technological development by scanning through the *Infrastructure* section of *Society*.

After searching for logical economic linkages between these countries, do you think that alliances such as the G-15 are good strategies for countries like Zimbabwe and Jamaica? Which country has the largest city? Does this correlate with that country's economic standing in comparison with its member nations? With increasing urbanization, problems, as well as progress, may develop. For a good example of this, visit Dakar via *Sights and Sounds* for Senegal. Why is rural-to-urban migration on the increase in these countries and what are the consequences? In your opinion, which of the G-15 countries has the greatest potential for technological advancement and which do you believe will continue to lag the furthest behind and why?   What should they bank on in the future?

Keywords: economic development, G-15, imports, exports, technology, urbanization

Geography is Very Spatial To Me!

When Taaffe, Morrill, and Gould developed their now-famous network model, they based their ideas on transportation development and change in West Africa. The model is best applied to colonial experiences where settlement first occurred on a coastline and later moved toward the interior of the landmass. Take a moment and review the model (Figure 5.9) and the discussion of Taaffe model in your textbook. Could you apply the model to the United States today? Let's "route" around and see what we can find.

Let's look at four states, Alaska, Minnesota, Tennessee, and New Jersey. Each of these will represent one of the four sequenced phases of the Taaffe network model.

Alaska may very well be our final frontier. Create a map of the state using the *Find Places* option. What we want to do is see if Alaska would make a good example for the "local ports' stage of the Taaffe model. Locate the Seward Peninsula either by zooming in on Nome or by using *Find*. Beginning at Nome and working eastward, write down the names of all the towns you find along until you finally reach Elim. How would you describe the transportation network in the southern half of the Seward Peninsula? Click on the largest town (and the one with the highest route density within the local area), go to *Web Links* and select the *Alaska Travel Guide*. What type of transportation is promoted at the very outset of this article? Why does this mode of transportation seem favored over others? What precipitated the development of a narrow-gauge railroad? What factors continue to inhibit highway network development in this region and all of Alaska?

The second stage of Taaffe's network model is penetration lines. The desire to exploit the interior is normally the impetus behind the development of penetration lines. We can see this firsthand by taking a trip to Duluth, Minnesota using the *Find Places* tool. Check out the city's transportation network by selecting *Web Links* and clicking on *The City of Duluth*. Scroll down to *Transportation in Duluth* and click to learn about the city's network development. You can also select *Duluth Infrastructure* for a additional background information. You should also investigate Duluth's sister city, Superior, Wisconsin located just to the south. Read *Geography* to get a better understanding of how these two port cities increased in size and economic significance by being connected to interior resources. What types of products are shipped through Duluth and Superior? How is this different from the ports on the Seward Peninsula?

Let's use Tennessee as an example of the network interconnection phase. In this third stage of the model, feeder lines extend from interior cities thus facilitating the expansion of their umlands. The elongated shape of this state and its three distinct

204

regions help as we attempt to show how distance and competition are interrelated. Create a map of Tennessee and using *Geography*, determine which are the three largest cities in the state. Then click on each city to learn more about their economic profiles. Which of the three has the most network connections? Care to predict which city is poised for the greatest growth thanks to its position within the network?

If it's "high priority linkages" you are looking for, go no farther than the New Jersey roadmap you can access through *Web Links*. Select *State of New Jersey* and then click on *Transportation*. Request a road map of the state and prepare to untangle a maze of federal and state roads. But through this maze, you find several high volume highways including I-95, I-195, I-295, I-80, and the New Jersey Turnpike. Several major port cities are linked through this network---can you name them? The New Jersey highway system provides crucial network connections between Pennsylvania, New York, Delaware, and of course, itself. The highways are major arteries that keep the "Boshwash" megalopolis going. And if you have ever been caught in a stopped traffic on any of those throughways, you will truly understand the meaning of high priority linkages!

Keywords: Taaffe's Network Model, transportation, Alaska, Duluth, Tennessee, New Jersey, umland

The Root of the Canal System: Erie, Isn't It?

In addition to his network model, Edward Taaffe also examined four eras of transportation development in the United States from an historical perspective. An understanding of the temporal changes in transportation access and innovations will lead you to a much broader interpretation of economic and social evolution. An excellent example of this is the history and legacy of the Erie Canal that is the hallmark of the Taaffe's "trans-Appalachian" era of transportation network development. So grab your mule and let's take a trip on the Erie Canal.

The Erie Canal was completed in 1825 and had a dramatic effect on the flow of goods and people from east to west. Locate the canal by using *Find Content*. To tour the canal and the surrounding regions, select *Web Links* and click on *Erie Canal History*. While you have the page open, scroll down to link to the *New York State Canal System* official homepage and click on the *History* icon. Read all about the development of the canal and its subsequent economic and social impacts. What advantages did the canal have over turnpike routes like the National Road? Where were the "Northwest Territories" and why would anyone want to go there? What is a "granary" and why did Governor DeWitt Clinton envision New York City as the "granary of the world?" How did the Erie Canal affect the economy and growth of New York City? Look at Figure 7.5 in your text. How does the import hinterland of New York City relate to its position on the canal system? How is the population distribution of New York State influenced by the canal even to this day? What event in 1959 resulted in the commercial decline of the Erie Canal? What types of economic activities are most common along the Erie Canal today?

The Erie Canal also had a tremendous influence over the fortunes of Buffalo, New York. Buffalo became a "break-of-bulk" point based on its site and situation along the canal system. To get a feel for 19th century life in Buffalo, select the *Web Link*, *Low Bridge! The Erie Canal Homepage*, and click on *The Buffalo Harbor* and *The Infected District*. How did the natural environment, finances, and politics help establish Buffalo's position on the canal? What were some of the social costs incurred by Buffalo as a result of the canal? How did the waterfront area get the nickname, "The Infected District?" How did railroad network improvements change the role of the Erie Canal in Buffalo? Why isn't there a National Football League team called the "Black Rock Bills?" Now that would be "Erie!"

Keywords: Edward Taaffe, trans-Appalachian, Erie Canal, New York City, Buffalo, New York

Houston, We Have a Problem: Invasion of the Multiple Nuclei

Of the three classical urban land use models discussed in your text, Chauncy Harris and Edward Ullman's "multiple nuclei theory" may be the easiest to apply to the contemporary urban landscape. Your textbook authors list four reasons why such land use patterns emerge on page 146. Read through that section carefully for you are about to test these ideas using Houston, Texas as your location.

Create a map of Houston using *Find Places*. Click on *Geography* to learn about the city's morphology, in particular, zoning ordinances. With that bit of background, let's get to work. Print out a map of Houston and keep that handy. Another map you will want to have is found in the *City of Houston--Internet Connection Web Link*. Click on *Virtual Tour* and use this map to help you identify Houston's land use patterns. An additional map and some good background information on the city can also be found in the *City of Houston* Web page. Click on *Houston Resources* and select *Greater Houston Partnership*. This will give you several useful links through *Overview*. Click on *Map of Key Locations* and *History* for some excellent information. You might want to print that map out as well for future reference. Take a quick look around the city through *Sights and Sounds*. The satellite image of Houston may be of help a little later. Now, go to *Web Links* and select *Rough Guide to Houston* and click on the

208

Into City icon. Now you should have enough references to approach the problem at hand--applying multiple nuclei theory to a real-life situation.

Review all the maps and background information for Houston you have gathered through Encarta. You will also need your textbook handy to refer to the discussion on classical spatial structure (Figure 7.7). Based on this information, try to identify the land use "districts" as listed in Figure 7.7. Do some theorizing on your own--make educated inferences based on known land uses and spatial patterns. From the Web pages you know where the museums are located. What type of residential neighborhoods would you expect to find near a museum, or a shipyard, or heavy industry? Circle and label these areas. Does the emerging spatial pattern resemble the model for multiple nuclei theory or would "concentric zone" or "sector" theory be a better fit? How do you think the lack of zoning ordinances for most of Houston's history has affected land use?

Unless you have spent time in Houston, you may not get all the land use patterns exactly right but you should be in the right ballpark--or at least near the Astrodome!

Keywords: classic spatial structure, Chauncy Harris, Edward Ullman, multiple nuclei, land use, Houston, Texas

Here's the Rub: The Dutch Have to Modify Central Place Spacing

It isn't often that a theory developed under ideal circumstances and assumptions is applied verbatim in the real world. But, that's exactly what happened in the Netherlands when the Dutch wished to settle the land area that they had claimed from the sea. In 1932, the Dutch built a very long ditch or earthen berm that essentially enclosed what used to be an inlet in the North Sea called the Ziederzee. What is it called now? To find out, click on *Find* and *Countries* and bring up a map of the Netherlands. Now go to the sidebar labeled *Land and Climate* and click on it. In the text material that follows you'll find that the Zeiderzee is now called IJsselmeer. Gradually this area in the province of Flevoland will be drained and allowed to dry. The salinity of the water in the North Sea would make these areas unproductive for agriculture immediately. There are five large bodies of land that the Dutch by the 1980s had reclaimed from the sea. What do they call these large parcels of land? Just how much land has been reclaimed from the sea since the 1930s?

The first polder to be reclaimed and was the parcel where Emmelbord is located. Click on that city and bring up a larger scale map of the area to the east of Amsterdam. Do you see the long earthwork that was built to keep back the angry North Sea and create the IJsselmeer? What would it be like to drain such a brackish, mucky area that was formerly part of the North Sea? You might get an inkling of what it is like by clicking on *Sights and Sounds*. Now click on the slide entitled *Gathering Rushes on the IJsselmeer*. Be sure to read the caption carefully.

Unfortunately for illustrative purposes, not all of the towns and agricultural centers that the Dutch government located in the Emmelbord polder are still present on the landscape. The Dutch were quite taken by Christaller's *Central Places in Southern Germany* and spaced their agricultural villages exactly the same distance apart that Christaller found to be the case in southern Germany. However, some twenty years had intervened between the theory's publication in 1933 and the time that the first polder was ready for settlement. By the 1950s, more people owned automobiles in the Netherlands and would often bypass the nearby agricultural village center in favor of going to the larger central places a bit further away. Do you see how their actions conform to the improved consumer behavioral postulate of Rushton in which both town size and distance are important stimuli motivating people in their selection of central places at which to shop for goods and services? Even though some of the agricultural villages that conformed to Christaller's spacing for the lowest order centers in a central place hierarchy did not survive, spacing between remaining settlements on the polder is relatively close. How close? Move the mouse to the pull-down at the top of *Encarta* called *Tools* and click on *Measuring Rule*. Using the mouse to locate the town of Urk as the origin and Emmelbord as the destination, measure and record the straight-line distance that intervenes. Now measure and record the straight-line distance between Emmelbord and Lemmer.

Compare those figures with the spacing between settlements on one of the more recent polder reclamations. Focus on the largest center in this part of Flevoland called Lelystad. Measure and record the distance between Zeewolde and Lelystad using the measuring tool. Repeat this for Lelystad and Oronten. Approximately how much further apart are central places in this new polder than they are in the original? The Netherlands learned from its mistake of slavishly conforming to the distance of the classical theory. It also now realizes that Lelystad must be upgraded to the next level of the central place hierarchy and serve as the regional center for the three polders to which it is centrally located. Theory must sometimes be modifed to account for dynamic changes within central place systems.

Keywords: Netherlands, polders, central place theory, Lelystad

A Tale of Three Cities

Far from being the bedroom communities built in the
image of Levittown, New York, contemporary
suburbs are just as likely to be a place where you to
commute to work rather than just a series of
residential subdivisions. The most common
commuting pattern today is from suburb to suburb
rather than the traditional pattern of suburb-to-city.
You can get a feel for the economic significance of
suburbs from the employment data listed in Table 9.1
in your text. Let's take three employment categories
and find out which cities lost the most economic
power to their suburbs. The three we will use are
total employment, manufacturing, and retail trade
between the years 1976 and 1994.

The city with the highest overall job loss to suburban
employment was New Orleans. Use *Find Places* to
locate the city. Click on *Geography* and read some
background material on the city. When did
population and subsequently jobs begin their exodus
from New Orleans?

Denver lost a whopping 34 percent of its
manufacturing employment to its surrounding
suburbs between 1976 and 1994. Create a map of
Denver and zoom in for a close up look. Click on the
communities of Aurora, Englewood, Lakewood,
Littleton, and Wheat Ridge, using *Geography*, to find
out more about these Denver suburbs. What types of

products are manufactured in the Denver area? Does the nature of what is being produced foster the migration of manufacturing away from Denver? Which Denver suburb is the largest in population? Which has the most diversified economy? Which do you think is poised to create the deepest competition for future jobs?

Long the bastion of the central business district, retail trade has found a home in suburbs in the form of an artificial downtown--the shopping mall. Of the cities listed in Figure 9.1, Baltimore lost the greatest percentage (22 percent) of its retail trade to its suburbs (with Denver and New Orleans not far behind). What makes Baltimore so vulnerable to suburban retail centers? Create a map of Baltimore using the *Find Places* tool. Take a tour of the city via the *Rough Guide to Baltimore Web Link*. Click on the *Into City* icon. How did the fire of 1904 change the downtown? Why did it fail to cover? Does this relate to developments in early 20th century suburbanization? How does the author of this page describe the city's downtown shopping district? What recent projects in downtown Baltmore have taken place in lieu of retail development? Is this the wave of the future for the city or are they just fishing around for solutions to avoid becoming just another living urban museum?

On the positive side, two cities that fared the best in the urban-suburban competition for retail employment were New York and San Francisco. New York City lost only 10 percent of its retail trade jobs and San Francisco a paltry five percent. What

214

advantages do these bi-coastal cities have over Baltimore? Check them out through Encarta and see!

Keywords: suburbs, employment, manufacturing, retail trade, Denver, New Orleans, Baltimore

Run for the Border: NAFTA

Along the U.S.-Mexico border, there has emerged a whole new manufacturing frontier. Most of the plants are owned by companies headquartered in other countries and most employ low-wage, low-skill assemblers. These factories are known in the border region as maquiladoras and employ thousands of Mexican laborers. Multinational corporations (MNCs) have long established plants here to take advantage of cheap labor and proximity to markets and transportation in the U.S. and beyond. It is believed that the North American Free Trade Agreement (NAFTA) will result in a further entrenchment of this type of manufacturing location. But what are the consquences of the maquiladoras? Travel to Ciudad Juarez, Mexico, just across the border from El Paso, Texas to find out.

In many ways, the border region has been an industrial target region for years as manufacturers have been attracted to the available and inexpensive labor market in Mexico but also by weak environmental regulations and enforcement. It is hoped that the environmental policies in NAFTA will result in cleaner industries along the border but so far the progress has been slow. Create a map of Juarez using the *Find Places* option then click on *Web Links*. Go to *Cleanup Along US-Mexican Border Remains a Dream* and read of some of the serious water quality and health hazards effecting not only

Juarez, but Tijuana, and Nuevo Laredo. Be sure to click on the *Silva Reservoir* link for more information on the role NAFTA is playing in the fight to clean up residential and industrial waste. For another case study on how sewage and industrial waste related to maquiladoras, go to a map of *Tijuana.* Click on *Web Sites* and select *Tijuana River Pollution and Maquiladoras.* What is perceived as the main economic impact of Tijuana River pollution? Why is California concerned about pollution in Mexico? How has the pollution affected the health of children on both sides of the border?

Travel south from Juarez to the city of Chihuahua. Go to *Web Links* and click *Chihuahua Industrial Parks.* Which American-based companies have located manufacturing plants in the state of Chihuahua? Is the Chihuahua's growth related to NAFTA?

Cross the border to El Paso, Texas. Click on the map symbol for *El Paso* and go to *Web Links.* Select *El Paso* and find out more about the city. On that Web page, click on the *Maquila* link. What's the purpose of "bonding" a maquiladora? Why would the Mexican government want to enforce such a policy? What location factors attracted manufacturers to this region? What is the basic and non-basic employment impact of maquiladoras in Juarez? Are any negative impacts of maquiladoras mentioned on this site? Why do you think that is?

Keywords: NAFTA, maquiladora, manufacturing location, Juraez, El Paso, Tijuana, environment, pollution

217

Diamond in the Rough: Facets of Industrial Development

You might expect countries like the United States, Japan, and Germany, to be the world leaders in industry as a percent of their gross domestic product (GDP). Patterns of world manufacturing are constantly changing with prevailing economic conditions such as wages, labor availability, technology, taxes, and environmental regulations. So do you think you might know which country ranks first in percent of GDP earned from industrial output? You can check your intuition by creating a world map and selecting *Statistical* under *Map Styles*. Select *Choose Statistic* and click on *Economy* then *Gross Domestic Product, Industry 1991*. Which country is number one? As it turns out, it's really a tie between Botswana and the United Arab Emirates (UAE) but would you have ever imagined those two countries would come out on top? Scan down your list and find the highest ranked European country. Let's find out why these countries are ranked so high.

Go to a map of Botswana using the *Find* tool. Check out *Facts and Figures* for some background information. What are the major industries in Botswana? Read the *Infrastructure* section for Botswana by clicking on *Society*. How does Botswana's economy compare to other African nations? Why has the government encouraged

industrial diversification in the 1990s? Click on the
Polishing Diamonds in Botswana in the *Economy*
section. Why does South Africa have such influence
over the Botswana economy? Why do you think a
large middle class has yet to emerge in Botswana?
For more detailed information, go to *Web Links* and
select *Botswana Country Profile*. Click on *Economic
Overview, Economy, Business Opportunities and
Challenges, Manufacturing and Mining* and read
each section.   After mineral processing, what is
Botswana's next major industry? Which foreign
countries have made investments in manufacturing
and what is the primary export market? What are
some positive and negative aspects to investing in
Botswana?

Now let's compare Botswana to Switzerland,
Europe's leader in percent of their GDP generated by
industry. Create a map of Switzerland and click on
Facts and Figures. Do you see any similarities in
terms of exports? How do the two countries compare
in basic demographics? Which has a higher per
capita GDP? How do the population growth rates
and infant mortality rates compare?   Which of these
two countries has the highest potential for further
industrial growth? In which sectors and why?

Keywords: manufacturing, Botswana, diamonds,
GDP, Switzerland

Hot Under the Crust: Geothermal Energy in Iceland

Alternative energy resources such as solar, wind, and geothermal power may hold the key to reducing our dependence on burning fossil fuels for electric power generation. As site-specific resources, they can only be exploited in distinct locations and each has its limitations. While many areas in the United States have the potential to exploit geothermal power, few in fact have taken advantage of this natural energy source. As illustrated in Figure 12.17 in your text, states like Idaho, Utah, and California have large regions with geothermal potential. Overall, less than one percent of all U.S. energy is generated via geothermal power plants but in other countries, naturally produced steam has been converted into a significant portion of their electricity needs. Take a trip to Iceland to learn more about how this island country copes with its energy demands by taking advantage of renewable energy sources.

Create a map of *Iceland* and select *Land and Climate*. Click on the first slide you see, *Icelandic Water Power*. Why you think Iceland has failed to fully take advantage of their hydroelectric power potential? Read about the country's *Economy* in *Society* for additional information. Now go to *Sights and Sounds*. Take a tour of the island and pay special attention to how the volcanic landscapes have shaped settlement patterns and economic activities.

How are hot springs utilized by Icelandic farmers to increase food production and grow exotic crops such as bananas in such a decidedly non-tropical location? What sorts of natural hazards are associated with geothermal regions? How have these both helped and hindered development in Iceland? What is possibly the only world's capital heated entirely by geothermal steam? Which city in the United States cited in your text had a similar system as early as the 1890s? Do you think geothermal steam is still used for that city's heating needs? Find out which alternative energy source is being touted by an Idaho utility by going to *Web Links* and clicking on *The Unofficial Idaho* then scroll down to *Utilities* and select *Idaho Power Company*. Click on the *Solar Energy* icon and select *Idaho Solar Energy Systems*. What is a "photovoltaic" system and why might such an energy source appeal to some Idahoans? Why would a public utility become involved in this type of technology? What advantages would this have over using geothermal power in Idaho? Do you think that Icelanders will be converting to solar power in the near future? Why or why not?

Keywords: geothermal power, energy alternatives, tectonic activity, volcanoes, Iceland, Idaho

"Real" Agriculture: Implosion or Explosion?

In 1970, the famous agriculture geographer John Fraser Hart, published a provocative article entitled "A Map of the Agricultural Implosion" in which he tried to define operationally what was meant by real agriculture (see Figure 13.22 p. 326 in Wheeler, et al.). He didn't want to include small plot cultivators or people who grazed a few head of cattle just because they enjoyed a semi-rural lifestyle. These people were hobby farmers and dabblers compared to the large agribusinesses that were making such an inroad on traditional agriculture as it had been practiced. Less than three percent of the gainfully employed persons in the United States are farmers but they produce more than 125 percent of the food we need each year. That makes farming in the United States a formidable commercial enterprise, the envy of many other countries.

Lacking any conceptual guidelines, Hart chose to map the percentage of farms in a county possessing gross incomes of more than $10,000 from the sale of farm products. Only if that percentage exceeded fifty percent was the county included in his definition of a "real" agricultural county. As can be seen by a perusal of Figure 13.22, real farm counties were rather limited in areal extent; certainly much less widespread than counties having some agriculture present. Five areas stand out most markedly: 1) the Corn Belt states of Iowa , Illinois, Indiana and nearby states; 2) the Central Valley in California, that irrigated paradise of specialty produce and cattle ranching par excellance; 3) the truck gardening areas of New Jersey, southeastern Pennsylvania, and the Delmarva Peninsula; 4) the Atlantic Coastal Plain region of the Carolinas known for cotton, tobacco, and hog production; 5) the lower Mississippi River valley famous for both soybeans and cotton. There were other locations outside of these five agglomerated clusters of counties but it was clear that big-time agribusiness was much more concentrated than agriculture as a whole. Is this still true?

Let's update Hart's groundbreaking study by playing detective. The U.S. Bureau of the Census conducts a Census of Agriculture every five years. The last year for which really complete data can be obtained is 1992. The 1997 Census is still not quite complete as of this writing. Click on *United States* in *Encarta* and then examine the *Web Links*. Click on the link to the *United States Census Bureau*. Then click on *Subjects A-Z* and click on *Agriculture*. Scroll down the options until you come to *NASS* (National Agricultural Statistics Service). Within the NASS, click on *Ag Census USA*. Then click on *1992 Ag Census*. You'll notice that one of the options is called *Agricultural Atlas of the United States*. That is where a geographer will often start (and sometimes end) a study. Once in the Atlas, you'll find all sorts of maps--some choropleth ones using county-level data and some dot distribution maps of more specific phenomena. Examine both types of maps for this activity.

Using the 1964 Census of Agriculture, Hart chose the value of sales of $10,000 or more as constituting commercial agriculture on a fairly large scale. With inflation, that figure would be meaningless today. Examine three dot distribution maps for the three highest categories of Farm Sales--Farms with Sales of $100,000 to $249,999: 1992; Farms with Sales of $250,000 to $499,999: 1992; and Farms with Sales of $500,000 or More: 1992. Note that because of the diminishing number of farms with large farm sales, the number of farms represented by each dot decreases as the monetary value of farm sales increase. The patterns are generally the same for all three maps. Where are the areas of high concentration of farms with large sales? Do these areas match the ones that Hart came up with using different statistics for the 1964 Census of Agriculture? Assuming success can be equated to farm sales, what differences do you detect between the pattern of modestly successful farms--those in the $100,000 to $249,000 category--and the extremely successful farms--those in the $500,000 or more category?

A better comparison with Hart's county-level data is obtained using two other statistics that the U.S. Census Bureau has recorded by county: 1) Percent of Farms with Sales of $500,000 or more: 1992, and, 2) Value of Sales from Farms with Sales of $100,000 or more as Percent of Total Value of Sales: 1992. Only 2.4 percent of farms nationwide had sales of $500,000 or more in 1992, but some counties had well over nine percent of farms that fell into the category (the darkest green category on the map). Are those counties in the region defined by Hart as practicing real agriculture in 1964? Are there some areas of the country that have been added or in which the value of farming has intensified in the almost thirty years that have transpired?

Interestingly, it appears that the Corn Belt of the agricultural Middle West, while a very important agricultural region, is still the domain of the large family-owned farm corporation. It appears to contain relatively fewer farms with sales over $500,000 than, say, the specialized agricultural cornucopia in the great Central Valley of California which is dominated as it is by really large growers.

In many counties the proportion of farms with sales of $100,000 or more in 1992 represented more than half of the farms in the county (i.e. the highest class interval shown on the second map described above). Why do you think there has been a relative agricultural intensification in the Aroostook County area of northern Maine? What about the following areas that have also experienced a considerable amount of agricultural intensification in the past thirty years: 1) the floodplain of the Red River (of the North) that forms the boundary between North Dakota and Minnesota; 2) the Imperial Valley of southeastern California; 3) the Texas panhandle region; 4) the areas of eastern Washington and Oregon extending into the Snake River plain of Idaho; and, 5) the central and southern areas of Florida? What crop and/or livestock combinations are represented in these areas?

Keywords: Agricultural Implosion, Agribusiness, United States, Central Valley (California), Corn Belt

How Now, Dairy Cow?

It may be time to loosen the traditional "dairy belt."
The major dairy states by numbers of cows or pounds
of milk produced are no longer necessarily located in
the historical diary belt as illustrated in your text in
Figure 13.17. The pattern as shown does not include
some major dairy states outside the northeastern core
region. When you think of dairy production which
state comes to mind--probably not Arizona or
California. You most likely think about Wisconsin,
the state whose license plate reads "America's
Dairyland." That's a very intuitive guess since
Wisconsin ranked number one in the number of milk
cows in the most recent United States Department of
Agriculture census. But the states that rise to the top
of the dairy industry in the amount of milk produced
per cow and total milk production are not in the
Great Lakes region. Let's find out more about the
structure of the American dairy industry through
Encarta until the cows come home.

Create a map of Wisconsin using *Find Places*, click
on *Web Links* and select *Badger: State of Wisconsin
Information*. From that Web page, go to *Wisconsin
State Agencies* and select *Agriculture, Trade and
Consumer Protection, Department* then select
Wisconsin Agricultural Statistics Service. Now you
can link to *Wisconsin Agricultural Statistics
Publications* and click on *1997 Wisconsin Dairy*

Facts. You will able to milk this page for gallons of information!

Check out *Dairy Highlights* for Wisconsin. Would it be fair to say that the state might be the "big cheese" in the dairy industry? Certainly Limburger lovers must find the state a ripe spot for their particular tastes in cheese! Now that you have some background on the dairy industry in Wisconsin, let's see how this state compares to the rest of the United States. Scroll back up the page and select *Top Twenty U.S. Counties in Milk Cow Numbers*. Which states are represented in the top ten? When does a Wisconsin county enter the rankings? Which county on the list has the most productive cows, averaging 21,200 pounds of milk per cow? Now let's look at another statistics table. Click *on Leading States, Milk Production Per Cow* (note: it may be helpful for you to print these tables out for reference and comparison purposes). You can see from this list that Wisconsin does indeed rank first in the U.S. in numbers of milk cows with nearly 1.5 million head. But which state ranks first in average milk production per cow? Which state ranks first in millions of pounds of milk produced? How does your home state compare with these locations? Conversely, which state ranks 50th in numbers of cows and production but manages to rank 12th in milk produced per cow? How might you explain that statistical relationship?

Now let's look at a broader issue in the American dairy industry--supply and demand. Modern dairy farmers have become more efficient than ever in increasing per cow milk production. The amount of fluid milk produced per cow in the 1990s has nearly

227

doubled since the 1960s, but at the same time the per capita consumption of fluid milk and cream has declined by 31 percent. See how this relationship has evolved over time by looking at the Web links for *Per Capita Consumption of Selected Dairy Products*, and *Milk Production-Wisconsin, Production, Historical*. In 1996, the average Wisconsin dairy cow produced 15,442 pounds of milk. If you think of the old adage, "a pint's a pound the world around" and picture the milk produced as 15,442 pint cartons of milk it might be a little easier to imagine exactly how much milk that is. How much milk did the average cow in Wisconsin produce in 1925? The difference in production can be attributed to over 70 years of improved dairy science, selective breeding, herd management, farm and herd size, as well as technological advancements in general. Consider that you could pour two eight-ounce glasses of milk from each pint, and multiply that by the Wisconsin average of 15,442 pints, how many glasses of milk would that be? That was just from one cow! Drinking two eight-ounce glasses of milk a day, how long would it you to consume the milk produced from just one Wisconsin cow? How many glasses of milk do you drink in a day?

While only 37 percent of all milk produced in the U.S. is marketed as "fluid milk" (like the gallon of milk you purchase at the store), when you multiply that out by the 154,331,000,000 pounds of milk produced each year--well, you can certainly say America's dairy farmers, "Got Milk!"

Keywords: dairy belt, fluid milk, Wisconsin, dairy cows

228

Part Five

Activities for *Contemporary Europe* Using Encarta® Virtual Globe

From Steel Girders to Fiber Optics: Origins of the European Union

The European Union represents one of the most potent and wealthy trading blocs in the world and yet its origin is a humble as a lump of coal and a chunk of iron ore. For indeed, of the many precursor organizations of the present European Union (EU), it was Robert Schuman's enlightened plan that got the whole ball rolling. Schuman was the secretary of state for West Germany when, in 1953, he saw the importance of one of the three bases for human interaction--complementarity. As described by the geographer Edward Ullman, complementarity is the basis for interaction that is most related to the economic principles and supply and demand. If one country has a resource in abundance that is needed by a neighboring country and, in turn, that same country lacks another resource that the neighboring country could provide, there exists a complementary basis for trade. It certainly doesn't mean that trade between these countries is inevitable. It just means that the conditions for trade or exchange are right from an economic (i.e., supply and demand) perspective. Perhaps the neighboring countries don't like each other very well and have had a long and bitter history of animosity towards one another. Their strained social relations may impede interaction even though economic forces may favor such an exchange. Such was the situation between France and West Germany. The two neighboring countries had fought a series of long and bitter wars (e.g., the Franco-Prussian War, World War I, World War II) in which they found themselves on the opposite side of the battlefield and old animosities die away slowly. But, the basic economic fact of life was that Western Germany, despite its abundance of coal suitable for conversion into coke, a fuel needed in iron and steel blast furnaces, lacked large supplies of iron ore. Much of Germany's coal was found in the Saarland area very near the French-German border. On the other hand, the Alsace-Lorraine district of France near the German border, contained abundant supplies of iron ore but the country had precious little coal. Aha! A complementary basis for exchange existed between the two former enemies.

Tariff barriers were already being lowered among the nations of Europe thanks to the passage of the General Agreement on Trade and Tariffs (GATT) in 1948. Eventually six countries signed the agreement that created the European Coal and Steel Community (ECSC). Sometimes referred to as the "inner six" they included France, West Germany, Italy and the Benelux countries (Belgium, Netherlands, and Luxembourg). Italy was blessed with an abundance of cheap hydroelectric power from the Alps that provided the electricity needed to operate electric arc furnaces in mini-mills located mostly in the industrialized northwestern part of the country. Belgium and Luxembourg had steel making capacity in place but many of the blast furnaces used older technologies and benefited greatly from the increased demand for European iron and steel.

To see how the "inner six" and many of the "outer seven" (the countries that formed the European Free Trade Association—the EFTA) eventually came together to form a superorganization, click on *Find* and then *Content* and type in *European Union*. What is the name of the treaty that created the European Union? When did it first become effective? When is the monetary union supposed to be formed? What was the immediate predecessor of the European Union? When was it created? In addition to the European Coal and Steel Community (ECSC), what other two organizations unified to form the organization that was the immediate predecessor to the European Union.

Former colonies of EU member countries receive preferential economic treatment. How many such countries are there? What was the treaty called that provided these trade benefits? Where is Lomé? (Hint: Use *Find* and *Places* in Encarta and then type Lomé). When the European Union combined with most members of the European Free Trade Association, what superorganization was created? What is its claim to fame?

Now click on the sidebar marked *Web Links*. Then click on the Web site marked *Europe Online*, the official web site of the European Union. Once there, click on *European Union* and then the *Euro*. Next, click on *One Currency for Europe* (in English or in any other language with which you have reading comprehension). You will see artists' renderings of the Euro notes that will eventually become universally accepted throughout Europe. What is pictured on the back of the 100-dollar Euro note besides an outline map of Europe?

Finally, click on *Euro Timetable*. On what date are the conversion rates of the present European currencies supposed to be irrevocably fixed and the legal status of the Euro approved? On what date will the Euro banknotes begin their circulation?

Keywords: European Coal and Steel Community, European Union, European Community, Euro

Alpine For You

When you mention "Alps" you naturally think of such locales as Switzerland and the peaks such as the Matterhorn. But there is another mountain chain by that name in Europe, the Dinaric Alps of Montenegro. The Dinaric Alps are situated on the Balkan Peninsula, a region know for its complex topography and equally difficult social and political history. Let's travel to this region and explore the physical geography of the Balkan Peninsula and discover more about Europe's "other" Alps.

Using the *Find Places* option, create a *Physical Features* map of the Balkan Peninsula. Select *Geography* and read the description of the region. How does the mountainous terrain affect this region's climate? Based on the discussion in *Geography*, how has the region's physical geography contributed to political instability and thus the geopolitical term, "balkanization?"

Now let's take a closer look at the Dinaric Alps by clicking on the map. Select *Geography* and read a detailed description of this mountain chain. What evidence is given to suggest that the Dinaric Alps are part of a karst region? What other "alps" are found in the vicinity? You can take a look at the Dinaric Alps by clicking on *Sights and Sounds*. As you read the caption, click on Montenegro that will take you to a map of that region and then select *Geography*. How did Montenegro get its name? How has the physical environment helped to create agriculture and settlement patterns? Now switch to *Web Links* and select *Montenegro at a Glance* and at the bottom of the page click on *Geography*. You can take a virtual tour of the region by clicking on the dramatic images of such locations as the Tara River and Durmitor Mountain. For additional details as well as slides and video clips, go to the *Ecological State of Montenegro* Web page by clicking on *Web Links* and click then on the *Scenery* icon at the bottom of the page. If you follow the links and view the images on this page, you will have some excellent details of how the physical environment of this region is inexorably tied to the human geography as well.

The Dinaric Alps are not as well known as the alps of Switzerland and Austria nor do they attract as many tourists. What factors inhibit tourism development in the Balkans? If you were developing a program to promote tourism in the Dinaric Alps region, which features would you choose to highlight and why?

Keywords: Dinaric Alps, Balkan Peninsula, Montenegro, karst topography

A Grecian Formula for Population?
The Graying of Europe

Among the many aspects of population discussed in Chapter 3 of the textbook, the one that stands in sharpest contrast is the difference in age structures. The affluent and well-established economies of Western Europe (with their increasingly older populations and low birth rates) are in stark relief to the less-affluent and emerging economies in some of the countries of Eastern Europe (with their younger and growing populations). Specifically, Albania is used as the example of the less-affluent, emerging nation. When the other nations of Eastern Europe were aligned with the Soviet Union, Albania was more influenced by the policies of the People's Republic of China. It has always marched to a slightly different drummer than some of its neighbors.

Let's compare Albania with some of its neighbors. First, click on *Find a Place* and then type in *Albania* to bring up a map of that country and its neighbors. What are the three countries that are contiguous to Albania? The area of (the Greater Serb Republic of) Yugoslavia has not published a complete set of recent demographic statistics. In this case, let's also compare Albania against Bosnia Herzegovina as well as the other two contiguous countries at its borders. One indication of a youthful but dependent

236

population is what demographers call the juvenility factor—the percentage of the population that is younger than 15 years of age. The implication is that children of this age are dependent upon their parents or other grown-ups to provide for them. They represent a bit of a drain on the society that must support them until they reach their productive working years. Using the *Map Styles* option select *Statistical*. When *World Stats* come up, click on *Population* and then the statistic *Population, age infant to 14, 1995*. A choropleth map of the region should be displayed. If you move the mouse around to the various countries in the region you will see listed the actual value of that statistic for the particular country. Albania has 31.4 percent of its population aged 0-14. Is that a higher or lower percentage than the contiguous and surrounding countries including Greece? What other country in the region displayed on the map of Albania and its surroundings has a juvenility value closest to that of Albania?

Now, let's examine the opposite side of the same population coin—the elderly population of these same countries. Stay within *Population* statistics but switch to *Population, age 65 and older, 1995*. We find that Albania has a value of 5.5 percent of its population in this age category. How does this compare with the surrounding and contiguous countries of the Balkan peninsular region? Why do you think that most of Albania's immediate neighbors have fewer young people (in a relative sense) and more elderly people than Albania? Again, what country in the region comes closest to the proportion of elderly people displayed by Albania?

Part of Turkey is in Europe and the largest portion is in Asia. As you travel further east into the heart of Turkey would we expect its age structure to begin looking more like Albania or more like some of Albania's neighbors (e.g., Greece, the former Yugoslavian Republic of Macedonia)? Why?

If Turkey and Albania are so close to each other in demographic structure, what do they think of each other? You might get a hint by clicking on *Sight and Sounds* and examining the caption of the image of the *Albanian capital of Tirané*. Do you think there is much love lost between these two countries if Albania has erected a *Museum of Struggle for National Liberation* from Turkey?

Keywords: Albania, Greece, Turkey, population, juvenility, elderly

Skirting the Issue:
Mini or Micro States?

Europe has sometimes been described as a patchwork quilt of former duchies, electorates, principalities, fiefdoms, and the like. Most of these tiny, formerly sovereign and autonomous political units were absorbed into one or another of the larger European nations. This process of consolidation picked up speed after the unification of both Italy and Germany in the 1870s. The transition from small autonomous units to the larger state into which most of these units were absorbed was not always a smooth one. As Cavour, the father of the modern Italian state once declared, "we have created Italy, now we must create Italians". Clearly there is a distinction to be made between the nation--a group of people that feel a strong sense of identity or affinity with one another-- and the state a geographic entity that usually contains within it more than a single nation. The textbook does an excellent job of describing many of the European nations that are, as of now at least, stateless (e.g., Basques, Friesians). What this exercise is designed to do is focus on the tiniest of states that somehow avoided amalgamation into some larger state entity. The smallest are the Vatican City, Monaco, Andorra, and San Marino.

Except for the "Babylonian captivity" of the papacy, when the center of papal control in the fourteenth century was shifted to Avignon, France, the Holy See has been in the Vatican City, an enclave of Rome itself. It is separate from the secular state of Italy that surrounds it because of its unique role as the home of the Pontiff (i.e., Pope) of the Roman Catholic church, a line of succession that goes back to St. Peter. Hence, the center of the Vatican City and its most important structure is the imposing St. Peter's Basilica. But what of the other three secular mini (or would they be micro?) states? What is their *raison d'etat*--their reason for separate existence? Let's start to answer that question by finding them on the map. Since they are so small, it would be best to go to *Find a Place* and then type in the name of each mini-state in turn. Where are Monaco, Andorra, and San Marino located? Which two are on border regions and which is an enclave? For each of the three mini-states, click on the *Facts and Figures* section and determine which of the three states is the largest. The smallest? Which one has the largest population (using the 1995 estimates)? The smallest population? And, finally, which one has been independent the longest? Is the United States as an independent state younger or older than these three mini-states?

Now turn to the *Sights and Sounds* section for each of the mini-states and answer the following questions. Examine the slide called *Andorran Storefront*. What language do most Andorrans speak? How does the language they speak relate to the percentage of Andorrans that can claim Catalan ancestry? Now examine the slide called *Andorran Street*. What is the name of Andorra's capital city? What does that name mean? (Hint: click on the capital city and then on the *Facts* locator for a translation). According to the slide called *High Andorra*, why was Andorra isolated for such a long time? What is the practice called of moving sheep and other livestock to high pasture in the mountains during the summer and back to protected valleys in the winter? What mountain range surrounds the principality? About how tall are these mountains? According to the slide called *Tourist Magnet in the Pyrenees*, what are Andorra's primary sources of income? Finally, the slide labeled *Tourism in Andorra* says that there are how many visitors to Andorra every year? How do you explain this large number if there are no airports or railroads to service these tourists? Do you think that Andorra's relative isolation well into the twentieth century adds to its present-day charm as a tourist destination? Why or why not?

Now turn to the slide entitled *Neighbors Chatting in San Marino*. In English, what is the official name of the republic? What was San Marino's stance during World War II? Did that stance keep its citizens from experiencing hardships during the war? Now turn to the slide simply labeled *San Marino*. The republic is located in the foothills of what mountain range? What draws tourists to San Marino? Where is the capital of the republic located? To which country is it economically most closely linked?

Finally, click on the image entitled *Café near the Grand Casino* (Monaco). Who designed this elegant building? What other famous building did he design? What is the period or style of architecture of which the Grand Casino of Monaco? In the slide marked *Gambling in Monaco*, what is the name of

the most elegant of all the casinos? When were the
first casinos legal in Monaco? What salutary effect
did they have on the citizens of Monaco? The yachts
in the slide called *Harbor of the Rich* belie a more
important historical aspect of Monaco's harbor?
Why was it fought over by so many Mediterranean
powers and felt to be of such strategic importance?

Keywords: Monaco, Andorra, San Marino, Vatican
City, mini-state

Oil and Water DO Mix: Petroleum Reserves in the North Sea

One of the greatest discoveries of oil in the last thirty years has been the bounty found in the North Sea. The technology to drill for oil and natural gas in the deep and sometimes treacherous waters of the North Sea and the Norwegian Sea of the north Atlantic required improvements in offshore drilling platforms and technology that has only come about since the 1970s. Figure 5-5 in the textbook shows a map of the discoveries to date. It also shows the territorial waters of each of the nation-states that borders the area. Notice that problem faced by countries that have a concave coast line such as Germany's border with the North Sea. Because of Denmark's Jutland Peninsula, Germany's stake is a small pie-shaped wedge into the North Sea. As of now, there is no known deposit of oil or natural gas in that sector of Germany's territorial waters. Sometimes territorial waters are allowed to extend to their maximum spatial extent of 200 miles from the coastline for economic purposes. In the North Sea this is not possible (see the scale of miles for Figure 5-5). In such a case, the common practice is to establish a median line between two countries so that the territorial sea can be shared equally. The boundary between the United Kingdom and Norway is an example of such a median line.

243

Now let's examine the nature of the resource base of the countries that face the North Sea. Create a map of Europe using the *Statistical Map* option. Which country that borders the North Sea produced the most metric tons of petroleum in 1993? Given their production, it is not hard to see why some of their detractors refer to them as the "blue-eyed Arabs of the North." What is the main source of electricity and power for factories, homes and commercial buildings in Norway? If you are not sure, choose *Statistics* and then *Energy and Minerals* and select *Electricity from hydroelectric sources in 1992*. With this relative abundance of cheap energy, what does Norway do with the oil and natural gas from the North Sea? Choose *Find* and then *World Stats.* How many metric tons of petroleum did Norway export in 1992? What percentage of total production of petroleum does this represent? To determine this, divide the total production of petroleum in 1992 by the amount exported in the same year.

On the other hand, how many million kilowatt-hours of electricity from hydroelectric sources were produced in the United Kingdom in the same year? What are the major factors that account for this disparity? Change the *Map Style* to *Physical* and compare the relative topography of the United Kingdom vis-à-vis Norway. Use the hypsometric tints of the Physical map to determine the highlands of Norway (browns and yellows represent uplands and shades of green are used to portray plains and fairly flat topography). What about the United Kingdom? Where are the highlands found on that island nation? If you said the Midlands region or England or Wales you are partially correct. But, the

Scottish Highlands seem to be the most rugged and, for many centuries, isolated.

Let's turn to Scotland for a minute. Only about one-tenth the population of the United Kingdom lives in Scotland, but the map of North Sea oil and gas deposits shows Scotland to be well-positioned to tap much of this richness. Do you think that this potential wealth has anything to do with the limited home rule that the new Labour government under Tony Blair has granted Scotland? Do you think the presence of oil and natural gas in Scotland is fueling the fires of the Scottish independence movement? If Scotland were to pull away from the United Kingdom and form itself as a separate sovereign nation, might it be a wealthy one? Why or why not?

Keywords: Scotland, Norway, the North Sea, petroleum, natural gas

How Did Brussels Sprout? Urbanization in Belgium

Sometimes professional geographers can be dumbstruck by data that they hadn't really thought about in any systematic way before. The data presented in Table 6-2 of the textbook is an example of this. It is clear that city-states such as Monaco and the Vatican City would be 100 percent urban. But Belgium! Industrialized and heavily urban certainly. But is it possible that Belgium is 97 percent urban when the average for all of Europe is already a healthy 73 percent? Can it really be that only three percent of Belgium's population lives in the countryside? Let's investigate by looking at *Encarta* for clues. Click on *Find* and then *Country* and type in *Belgium*. The map will show that Belgium is divided into two major regions. What are they? Now click on *Facts and Figures* on the sidebar. What are the five largest cities in Belgium? What proportion of the total population of the country is accounted for by these five cities? To answer this question you must cumulate the sum of the population of the five cities (figures for the cities are not completely compatible time-wise) and then divide that number by the population of the country as a whole. Even more than the United States, the population of Belgium's top cities seems to conform to the rank-size rule. This regularity, investigated extensively by the sociologist George K. Zipf and the geographer Brian J.L. Berry, states that in many

246

advanced countries, the population of a city of rank n can be estimated by dividing the population of the first ranked city (e.g., Brussels) by n. How well does Belgium conform to this regularity (at least for the first five ranked cities)? Berry noted four circumstances under which the rank size rule was a likely outcome—the country was large, it had a diverse and complex economy, it had a long history of urbanization, and had not been subjected to colonialism in the recent past. How many of these criteria fit the Belgian case? What is the source of the data on population? How does the United Nations define the term "urban"?

Now, click on *Society* on the sidebar for more information about Belgium. From what tribe or group are the Walloons descended? What percentage of the total population in Belgium is accounted for by the Walloons? Where are the Walloons geographically concentrated? What language do most Walloons speak? What religion do they embrace? What is another common name for the Flemish region of Belgium? From what group or tribe are the Flemish descended? What language do they speak? Interestingly, almost ten percent of Belgium's population is made up of immigrants. What are the major source areas for these immigrants? If Dutch is spoken in Flanders and this region accounts for over one-half of the entire population of the nation, why is it that over three-fourths of Belgium's population embraces Roman Catholicism. If the Dutch were influenced by John Calvin and are largely members of the Protestant Reformed Church, why isn't Belgium, especially the Dutch speaking part, more heavily Protestant?

Continuing in *Society,* find out what unofficial Belgian holiday comes closest to our own Groundhog Day. Instead of "Puxatany Phil" being the official weather prognosticator, who or what serves the purpose of weather forecaster in Belgium? What type of weather event is being predicted? On what day do Belgian children look forward to receiving a Belgian waffle? What about the town of Binche reminds one of Rio de Janeiro in Brazil? Click on *Sight and Sounds* and then peruse the slide entitled *Carnival Celebration* and accompanying *Carnival music*. Is this holiday pagan or Christian or both? Now turn to the slide of *Brugge by Boat.* Why did Brugge lose the prominent position it held in the 14th century? What feat of modern engineering has been used to overcome the earlier ecological disaster? So, where are those three percent of rural folks located exactly?

Keywords: Belgium, Brussels, rank-size rule, Brugge

Planting the Garden Cities of Tomorrow: Avoiding Urban Anarchy in the UK

Allusions to the best known song of the Sex Pistols
notwithstanding, this activity is not about Johnny
Rotten or Sid Vicious. Rather, it's about an urban
visionary named Ebezener Howard. Perhaps if the
United Kingdom had heeded Howard's warnings
about the evils of urban sprawl and decay sooner,
there would have been no need for a punk movement.
So, indirectly this exercise is about the condition of a
society that spawned the punk movement and large
amorphous cities such as London that defy the
human scale. Earlier we learned that Belgium's cities
conformed reasonably well to the rank-size rule.
What about the cities of the United Kingdom? Click
on *Find* and then *Places* and type in *United
Kingdom*. London and its immediate environs
certainly do take up much of southeastern England.
What are some of the other large cities in the United
Kingdom? Click on the *Facts and Figures* sidebar in
order to answer this question. What percentage of the
United Kingdom's total population is accounted for
by the top five cities (again, ignore the data
comparability problem of population estimates taken
at different time periods)? How does this percentage
compare with the same percentage that you
calculated for Belgium? Even though they are
roughly the same (in both cases about one-fifth of the
country's population lives in the top five cities), does

the United Kingdom conform to a rank-size distribution? If it did, how large would Manchester be? No, London is clearly predominant. This city size distribution is called primate because the dominant city is so much larger than any other urban center. It has been argued that primacy is indicative of a lesser-developed economy and rank-size is indicative of advanced economic development. If that is true (and the hypothesis is certainly suspect), the United Kingdom is certainly a glaring exception to the generalization.

London was so big and so spread out that after World War II, that the government decided to do something about it. They created a series of new towns to act as counter-magnets to continued in-migration to London and other large cities in the United Kingdom. What is the oldest new town? Examine the map in the book (Figure 7-12) to determine the answer. In that year, the government passed the Greater London Plan which created a stop-line of development beyond which would be established a green belt. Within this green belt, which might be twenty miles wide, the only allowable land uses were agriculture, recreation, and open space. London was no longer free to sprawl all over southeastern England. Beyond the green belt, a series of new towns were planned for greenfield sites. These new towns were reminiscent of an idea developed by the planner and visionary Ebenezer Howard in the late 19th century. Howard felt that the city was becoming too dense, polluted, crime-ridden, and dysfunctional. On the other hand, rural life was far from the bucolic existence portrayed in the landscapes of famous British artist Thomas Hogarth and others earlier in the 18th and 19th centuries. Rural areas were regions of unemployment and underemployment and were increasingly ineffectual in keeping young people on the land and away from the lure of the big city lights. Howard proposed new towns that would combine the best of the town and the country together. They would create a sense of community often missing in the isolation of the countryside and the alienation of the big city. They would also be tied into nearby large cities by high-speed ground transportation such as a commuter railroad. But, many of the people who might live in these new towns would also work there. These weren't to be just ordinary bedroom communities. They were to have a viable employment base of their own. Click on a map of *London* and you will note that all of the new towns are outside of the square that defines the greater London area. Which new town is named after a famed British economist? Which one sounds like it might have been named after a 1930s blonde who was a movie sex symbol? Unfortunately, there are no detailed maps of these new towns in *Encarta* so it is not possible to tell whether they remained true to Howard's vision of the separation of vehicular and pedestrian traffic--with lots of open green spaces for citizens to commune with nature. It appears that many of these new towns greatly exceed the population limits of between 30-50,000 that Howard had in mind. Besides London, what other cities in the United Kingdom also have new town developments? In the meanwhile let's have a look at one of the problems faced by London today. Click on *Sights and Sounds* on the sidebar and go to the slide labeled *London's ethnic diversity.* What percentage of London's population is made up of immigrants?

How extensive was the British Empire (now the British Commonwealth of nations)? Might visible and segregated ethnic communities engender feelings of animosity among some working class British youth who find it hard to break into the ranks of the employed when they are competing against recent immigrant arrivals for jobs? Feelings of hopelessness and despair about Britain's declining world position in the post-war world were at least some of the motivating forces behind the punk movement of the 1960s and '70s. Do you think the new town movement improved the prospects of British youth? Why or why not?

Keywords: new town, Ebenezer Howard, primate city distribution, green belt, Greater London Plan

A Jug of Wine, A Loaf of Bread, and Encarta: French Viticulture

Fine wines are so closely associated with French culture that sometimes we forget that the physical environment and marketing conditions are also central to wine production. The French landscape in many areas is a living history museum of viticulture. Many types of wines are named after locations in France such as Champagne and Cognac. A virtual tour of French wine regions will give you greater insight as to the geographic nature of viticulture as well as the cultural and economic roles of wine in France. Begin your visit in Burgundy. Use the *Find Places* tool to create a map of the Burgundy region. You can view a Burgundy vineyard by selecting *Sights and Sounds*. Next, click on *Web Links* and select *Wine Regions of France*. You will use this extensive Web site to tour France's wine regions.

Begin your tour with a review of the French wine industry by clicking on *History*, *Geography*, and *Economy*, on the homepage. You should be able to see how changing political and technological conditions affected the French viticulture. Vineyards in France managed to survive Roman invaders and even the French Revolution but how did a transportation innovation threaten to bring the wine industry to a grinding halt? The natural environment figures heavily in the success of France's vineyards. How does France's physical geography create favorable conditions for viticulture? What are the

253

two soil prerequisites for growing high quality grapes? The French drink more wine per capita than any other country except perhaps Italy, but why has consumption declined since the 1970s?

Now turn your attention to the map of France on the *All About Wine* homepage. You can click on each of the wine regions for more detailed information. For each of the regions you should read through the narrative and then answer the questions below.

Burgundy
How did the diffusion of Christianity and the establishment of a French monarchy aid the development of Burgundy wines?

Champagne
 What types of soils are best for producing champagne grapes? How are these similar or different from those found in the Burgundy region? What makes the soils of the Champagne region suited for this sort of cultivation? How does the history of *Reims* figure into the development of Champagne?

Cognac
How did trading patterns in the Cognac region and North Sea merchants help to shape Cognac's specialized wine industry?

Provence
What role did the port of *Marseilles* play in the development of the Provence wine region? What climate type is associated with Provence? Why are this area's vineyards often situated on south-facing slopes?

Loire

Why were the Dutch interested in Loire valley viticulture? How is this pattern similar to that of the Cognac region?

Jura

Jura wines may not be as well known as those from other regions in France, but which famous scientist hailed from this area where he experimented with fermentation processes?

Alsace

How has the tug of war over Alsace between France and Germany affected the region's wine production? Why are Alsace vineyards located on the eastern slopes of the *Vosges Mountains*?

Beaujolais

How did an ancient Roman road and later, a group of Benedictine monks, help create Beaujolais wines? How do the Beaujolais Hills work to both help and hinder vineyard production?

Savoie

Taking into consideration its location, why would Savoie vineyards be best located on the south or southwest facing slopes of mountains and which mountains would these be?

Rhone

Why might scholars believe that the vineyards of the Rhone region would be the oldest in France? What is a *galet* and how does it influence viticulture in the southern Rhone valley?

Languedoc-Roussillon

How did transportation innovations expand markets for Languedoc-Roussillon wines? How did vineyards of Languedoc-Roussillon recover from the devastating effects of *phylloxera*? What is a *tremontane* and how is it different from a *mistral*?

Armagnac

What do Armagnac and Cognac have in common? How does Armagnac's location increase the vineyards' risk for storm damage?

The Southwest

What do *Bergerac*, *Cahors*, *Agen*, and *Galliac* all have in common?

Bordeaux

What do Bordeaux, the West Indies, and Dutch traders have in common? If Bordeaux is situated in the same latitudinal extent as Maine and Nova Scotia, why is the former so well suited for viticulture while the later two locations are better known for potatoes and commercial fishing?

After reading through such an extensive discussion of the wine industry in France, you may not become an expert on French wines but you probably have a better understanding of how and why viticulture has flourished there for centuries.

Keywords: France, wine, viticulture, soils, climate

Leaving Their Denmark:
The Far-Flung Faeroes
Without Pyramids

Sometimes photographs of places can excite the imagination. Especially when they are of exotic and faraway places. And then again sometimes the photographs are so grim, you wonder how anybody in their right mind would want to live in the place shown much less visit as a tourist. We got that feeling when we saw the photograph of a small settlement in the Faeroes, a far-flung group of islands that were, millions of years ago, part of the island nation of Iceland. Take a look for yourselves at Figure 9-8. The landscape looks really bleak and barren and yet, the caption of the photograph suggests that the climate is mild but too cool for tree growth. How can a climate be mild on the one hand and yet prohibit tree growth (except on the lee side behind the protective barrier of houses and outbuildings)? Let's see what we can find out about this isolated island group. Click on *Find* and then *Places* and type in *Faeroes*. What is the capital of the Faeroes? No, it's not Cairo, Alexandria or Luxor; it's Torshaven, which probably translates as "Thor's harbor" so be careful not to disturb the god of thunder. Click on the sidebar called *About the Map.* Examine the symbols for depth of ocean water. The palest blue color is reserved for water that extends only to 50 meters in depth. How extensive are such shallow waters off of the Faeroes? The next blue

257

hypsometric tint shows water that is deeper than 50 meters but less than 200 meters in depth. Using the scale of miles on the map of the Faeroes, how far would you estimate this relatively shallow water extends? Any water that is less than 200 meters in depth (about 650 feet) can be penetrated by sunlight and, therefore, can provide the breeding ground for plankton and other sea creatures at the lowest end of the food chain. It appears that the Faeroes are also a location where a warm water current (the same one that comes from the Gulf Stream of coastal Florida) meets with the much colder Greenland current. When two such currents meet, a great deal of upwelling occurs that stirs up the nutrients in the water making excellent breeding grounds for fish. How important do you think fishing is to the people of the Faeroes? Click on the sidebar marked *Sights and Sounds* and let's see if we can gather any clues. The middle slide in the set is called *Life in the Faeroe Islands*. Now, is it just us, or is it the color photography? Doesn't the locale look a lot more inviting than the black and white photograph in the textbook (Figure 9-8)? In fact, if the caption were missing, the slide looks like it might have been taken at some Norwegian fishing village along the fjords or along the waterways of Copenhagen, Denmark. Wait. Denmark. What exactly is the relationship of the Faeroes to Denmark? Move the slide set to the one entitled *Green Cliffs of the Faeroe Islands*. What does the caption to the photograph imply about status of the Faeroes? It is just a little mysterious, don't you think? Are they independent or not? For further elaboration, click on the sidebar for *Geography*. According to the information provided, when did joint control of the islands between Norway and

258

Denmark end and the sole sovereignty of Denmark begin? When did the parliament of the Faeraoes (the Lagting) declare independence of the islands from Denmark altogether? What compromise was worked out two years later? Who controls the islands' foreign relations? Are the Faeroes allowed to print their own money, raise their own flag and speak their own language? What language is it that they speak? Within the material on *Geography* we find that the islands are of volcanic origin. We also are given a reason why the islands were initially treeless despite the reasonably mild temperatures. What is the reason?

Now click on the sidebar called *Sights and Sounds* and let's take a virtual tour of the Faeroes. No, there is no Valley of the Kings here, but there might be a fjord of the gods. Click on the slide entitled *Green Cliffs of the Faeroe Islands* and, if your computer is equipped for sound, play the ballad too. According to the text in the figure caption, such ballads were written for community events and community dances are still held. In a recent survey poll, people from Iceland were voted the happiest people on Earth. The Faeroes are geologically speaking, part of Iceland and they are protected from the bitterness of the climates normally associated with such a northerly latitude by their maritime location. It is their proximity to the warm water current from the Gulf Stream that becomes the all-important North Atlantic drift. Without it, the climates of Iceland, the Faeroes, and indeed all of Europe would be much harsher and subject to more extremes of temperature than they are now. How would you describe the music you hear on the ballad? It's not exactly Weezer, but the music of the Spaelmenniner group is still quite engaging--perhaps because of the blend of primitive and modern instruments. Move to the *Hay Harvest* slide. What percentage of the islands' land area is devoted to agriculture (i.e., arable)? Why do you think that fish have become a more important commercial product for export than the sheep that are raised there? What does the original name of the island (i.e., *Faereyiar*) mean? Who first settled the Islands and when? Now, click on the sidebar for *Animals*. What animal is shown in the slide and why is it so important to the people of the Faeroes?

Finally click on *Web Link* and then again on a site entitled *Our Trip to the Faeroe Islands*. This link is the next best thing to you showing your vacation photographs to family and friends. The pictures appear to belong to Andreas Bjornberg who goes to Halmstad University. Although the quality of the color photos is not as good at the ones used in the *Sights and Sounds* slide set, they do convey a definite and largely positive impression. Note especially the mystical grotto carved by the wind and sea into the fjord-studded coastline. Notice the waterfall in the background? Have the Faeroes moved up on your 'must see' list of exotic places around the world that you'd like to visit? Why or why not?

Keywords: Faeroes, Denmark, Norway, Gulf Stream, fishing

Malta Milks Tourism

Such diverse groups as Phoenicians, Greeks,
Normans, Arabs, Ottomans, and the French have
imprinted the history of Malta. The last foreign
power to control the Mediterranean islands were the
British who departed when Malta gained
independence in 1964. With so many cultural
influences and its favorable Mediterranean location,
Malta appears to be a natural for tourism
development. Let's take a tour of Malta and learn
more about its history and contemporary landscape.
First, create a map of Malta by using the *Find Places*
option. Select *Land and Climate*, *Facts and Figures*,
and *Society* for some solid background information.
What are the two economic sectors placing the
greatest demands on Malta's water supply? Why
does Malta suffer from fresh water shortages? How
will water problems affect future tourism
development? Why do you think British visitors
account for over half of all tourists to the islands?
Next, review the images in *Sights and Sounds*. How
could such a relatively small country have developed
such a diverse cultural landscape? Can you think of
any other European regions with similar historical
characteristics?

For a more in-depth look at Malta and its tourist
industry, switch your focus to *Web Links*. First,
select *Facts About Malta*, the official government
Web page for Malta, and select *The Maltese Islands*.
Click on *Location, Area, and Climate*. Which

environmental factors did the government chose to highlight? How is the island of Gozo introduced to the reader? Do you think this is an accurate description and if so, why would Gozo be of interest to tourists? Now go back to the Maltese government home page and select *Land and People* and then *Malta Tourist Information*. What are some of the country's features that the government chooses to promote as tourist destinations? According to the government, how did events in Maltese history create a tourist-friendly environment?

A second Web page to view is *Malta--Cradle of the Mediterranean*. Go back to the main listing of Maltese Web sites and select this page which focuses on tourism. Who is responsible for this Web page and why is that significant to know? Click on *Geography and Weather* and read the description of the physical environment. Do you see any similarities between this page and the official government site? Now go back and read through the remaining parts of this page. How are the people of Malta portrayed by the authors of this site? Why do they portray Malta as *The Perfect Winter Holiday Destination*? In which six countries would you find Maltese tourism offices? How does this fit within the government's marketing of Malta as a tourism center?

For such a small group of islands, Malta is packed with a wide variety of historical and cultural attractions. Favorable environmental conditions that prove attractive during the European winter season are certain to appeal sun-loving tourists. After reviewing many aspects of the Maltese islands, why do you think the government is so eager to push tourism as a major focus of economic development? Why would the government find tourism more attractive than industry or agriculture? Did the government-sponsored web pages sell you on a Maltese vacation?

Keywords: Malta, tourism, Gozo, water, Mediterranean, economic development

The Walls Come a Tumblin' Down: Will the Two Germanys Ever Be Truly United?

One of the most poignant moments in modern history were the days in the fall of 1989 when the Berlin Wall started to be torn down. It was indeed shades of the story of Joshua and the walls of Jericho from the Bible. But, instead of blasts from a ram's horn, it was the enthusiastic swing of pickaxes and sledgehammers of exuberant youth on both sides of the border that did the wall in. The wall, ordered constructed in 1961, had formally separated East and West Berlin. It was an ugly structure that did not remain a *tabla rasa*. Instead defiant students on both sides of the wall would paint graffiti on the wall calling for freedom and justice and a reunited Germany. That hideous graffiti-laced concrete and steel reinforced rod wall came down twenty-eight years after its hurried construction. In the days that followed the reunification of the two Germanys, the professionals came to finish the job begun by the youth. Bulldozers and heavy equipment replaced the pickax and sledgehammer. Those were heady days. A song written about the historic event even revived the sagging career of the German heavy metal group The Scorpions. Winds of change indeed. An entire generation of Germans had lived with their country rent asunder, resolutely divided between East and West, seemingly never to be united again.

But then began the hard part. For twenty-eight years, the countries had taken separate development paths toward economic progress—capitalism reigned supreme in the West and socialism in the East. For some in the East it was twenty-eight years of fear of the Stahsi (the East German secret police) and separation from extended families on the other side of the border. Most East Germans were clearly happy to see the leaders of their "socialist worker's paradise" ousted, but freedom came at a very high price. East Germany with its 17 million citizens was considerably poorer than its more prosperous and populous Western counterpart. Taken together, a reunited Germany with more than 80 million citizens is the most populous nation in Europe except Russia and arguably the most important. Its geographic location is central—balanced between the west and the east. And Berlin, the chosen capital of the reunified Germany, is its most visible city. Let's take a closer look at this city which was at one time the capital of the Prussian Empire, the capital of the Republic after WW I and now once again the capital of a reunified Germany. Click on *Find* and then *Places* and type in *Berlin*. The relatively detailed map you see before you shows both East and West Berlin. Locate *Checkpoint Charlie* on the map. It was the entry and exit point during the Cold War to the American sector of West Berlin. British and French forces controlled access to other sectors in West Berlin. Let's take a virtual tour of Berlin by clicking on *Sights and Sounds*. The first slide in the set is entitled *Turkish Store in Berlin*. Turks fill a valuable role within German society; often working in menial low-wage jobs that the Germans feel are beneath them. These gastarbeiter (guest workers) may stay a short time and then return to their homes in Turkey or North Africa or some of the poorer countries in the former Warsaw Pact nations of eastern Europe. Some Germans see these guest workers as part of the wrenching economic problems faced by Germany in the 1990s as it struggles to establish some semblance of parity between formerly poor East Germany and wealthy West Germany. There have been attacks on their housing compounds and neighborhoods; evidence that a neo-Nazi movement in Germany is, unfortunately, alive and well. The next slide is entitled *Traversing a Reunited Berlin*. What is the name of the river that runs through the city of Berlin? If your computer is equipped with sound what do you think of the free jazz movement in Germany? Compare that music with the grandiose sound from Beethoven's Ninth Symphony (the Ode to Joy) played while you admire the set piece of the former Prussian Empire, the *Brandenburg Gate (Brandenburger Tor)*. When was the Gate constructed? To find out where the Brandenburg Gate is located, return to the map of Berlin and find the centrally located green space where the Zoological Park (*Zoologischer Garten*) is located. This park is called the Tiergarten and that is where the Brandenburg Gate can be found. The next slide shows people taking a whack at the *Berlin Wall* in November of 1989. The city has left a few feet of the wall standing in various places around the city as a mute reminder of the Cold War period. The next slide shows the *Charlottenburg Palace (Schloss Charlottenburg)*, built by Frederick I for his bride Sophie Charlotte. When did Berlin become the capital of the Prussian Empire? What is the architectural style of the Palace? View the slide

Satellite View of Berlin. It's easy to spot the Brandenburg Gate and the Templehof Airport in the foreground of the SPOT satellite image. Now, let's check out the *Web Links* associated with Berlin. Click on *Expedia World Guide--Berlin.*, then on *Background* , and then *Overview*. Where did the name "Berlin" come from? How many people died attempting to cross the Wall between 1961 and 1989? What was the showcase boulevard of old Berlin? What did Hitler do with the lime (i.e., linden) trees that lined the broad avenue? Click on *Unter der Linden* for more *Historical and Architectural Sights* in Berlin. You may be familiar with the highly acclaimed German novel by Döblin entitled *Berlin Alexanderplatz.* What famous German filmmaker made a movie based on the novel? What is Alexanderplatz best known for now? What do Berliners call Alexanderplatz? What is the Weltzeituhr?

Suppose you were a citizen of the former East Germany (i.e., the German Democratic Republic). Before reunification you had a modest state-subsidized apartment to live in and you were guaranteed a job for life. Suddenly, you were cast into a larger society in which there are no job guarantees. You must compete in a labor pool that is somewhat distrustful of you and even makes fun of you. You are an Ossie, a resident of the former East Germany and they are Wessies and some of them think they are superior to you merely because of where you come from. Write a paragraph explaining how you feel about this abrupt transition in your life.

Keywords: Berlin, reunification, Prussia, Berlin Wall

Krakow's Holocaust Legacy

The city of Krakow is the third largest in Poland and may be the country's oldest urban settlement. Krakow has long been a cultural center in Poland, noted for its art and built environment. In many ways, the city is a living museum with many fine examples of medieval and gothic architecture. Unfortunately, many older structures are endangered as waves of urban renewal projects sweep over some sections of the city, while other suffer from neglect and industrial pollution. But Krakow has survived worse. The deepest scars suffered by Krakow came during World War II when German Nazis occupied the city and sent thousands of its Jewish residents to their deaths in nearby concentration camps.

To get a feel for the contradictions that are modern Krakow, use the *Find Places* tool and create a map of the city. Click on *Geography* and learn about the city's development. Select *Sights and Sounds* and view an image of *Wawel Castle* and listen to a sample of Polish folk music. Additional information about the cultural treasures of Krakow can be found by accessing several web pages. Go to *Web Links* for Krakow and first select *The Old Krakow*. This page includes some images from historic Krakow as well as a short narrative. What does the author of this page believe are the most serious threats to Krakow's cultural landscape? Additional information about the city's history can be accessed by selecting the *Some Words About Krakow* Web page. While this site gives a basic overview of the city's history, what major 20th century event is completely ignored? To make up for this oversight, go to the *Krakow* Web page for link to the city's Jewish history.

There are many good links on the Krakow page. Perhaps the best for our study would be the *March of the Living, 1994: Virtual Tour*. Click on this link and join a tour of Canadian Jews who came to Poland in 1994 to honor the memories of those who died during the Holocaust. Follow the first five parts of the tour (Parts 1-5). During the first part of the tour, what relics of the past did the marchers experience? Why did they find the display of souvenirs offensive? The second part of the trip included a difficult visit to Auschwitz-Birkenau where millions of Jews were murdered in gas chambers. What items were on display at the Museum at Auschwitz? What were Jewish ghettoes? Why did the marchers find the motto at the entrance to the camp ironic? As you go forward with the marchers through the remaining parts of the tour, which images or narrative descriptions affected you most?

The complete history of Krakow cannot be told or fully understood without integrating the story of Jewish history, culture, and tragedy. Krakow's pre-World War II Jewish population was large and made great cultural and economic contributions to the city. Today, only three Krakow synagogues survive, a city which prior to 1939, counted among its population 60,000 Jews, including those living in the nearby suburb of *Kazimierz*. What is the future of Jewish culture in Krakow? Take a moment and go back to the *Krakow* home page and click on *Krakow's*

Former Jewish District Offers Development Potential. What are the major problems facing developers in Kazimierz? What would be the financial benefit of developing a historic district in Kazimierz? Do you think that in the future Krakow will be able to market itself not only as a major cultural center for medieval architecture but also as a focal point for European Jewish history?

Keywords: Krakow, Poland, Jews, Holocaust, Kazimierz, Auschwitz

Unhappily Ever After?

How would you feel about getting married in a country where nearly three-quarters of all marriages end in divorce? Welcome to Estonia, where golden wedding anniversaries must be as rare as warm days during the long Russian winter. You can compare Estonian divorce rates with other social characteristics by reviewing Table 13-5 on page 611 in your textbook. In general, happily ever after is not commonly experienced in the Baltics. Take a moment and review all the statistics listed in the table. What conclusions could your draw from this information? Do you think there is any correlation between divorce rates and use of contraception or abortion? What do the rates of suicide reveal about life experiences in the region? Let's look at these Baltic Sea countries, Estonia, Latvia, and Lithuania, and try to find clues that would help explain why life can be so difficult for families living in this region.

Take a look at all three countries and Russia to compare their relative social conditions. First, create a map of each country using the *Find Places* tool. Click on *Facts and Figures*. Are there any statistics that may explain why life in Estonia, Latvia, and Lithuania may be more difficult here than in Russia or the other Newly Independent States (NIS)?   Now we need to take a more in-depth look at social conditions in each of these states. You can do this by selecting *Society* and reading about *Demographics* and *Marriage and Family* for each of the Baltic states and for Russia. What are the major demographic differences or similarities between each country? Which of the Baltic states has the highest percentage of ethnic Russians? Is there any relationship between ethnic composition and social characteristics? Which of the Baltics is most urbanized and which is most rural? Do you think that there are any linkages between urbanity and the social problems listed in Table 13-5?

Take a few minutes and read about *Marriage and Family* (for Lithuania, Estonia, and Russia) and other social characteristics of these countries as discussed in *Society*. Be sure to click on the wedding slides for Lithuania and Russia (in *Sights and Sounds*). How have religious practices changed in the Baltic region and Russia? As you compare religious participation between the four countries, do you think there is any correlation between religious beliefs and divorce? Why do you think it is fairly common for couples to live together prior to marriage? Would living with in-laws and parents be the ideal way to begin a life together? Why would moving in with parents be a popular option for many newlyweds? Would access to childcare facilities figure into housing decisions? What do the parents receive in return for their generosity?

After reading through the *Society* discussions for Estonia, Latvia, Lithuania, and Russia, can you draw any conclusions about family life and social conditions that might help explain the relatively high rates of abortion, children born outside of marriage, divorce, and suicide? How might access to medical care figure into this question? In these regions, does free medical care translate into each country having a healthy population---why or why not? What is the prevailing government's attitude toward abortion? Why would the abortion rates for these countries be higher than most industrialized countries? How would health problems such as alcoholism affect family stability?

Searching for the underlying causes of divorce or other social characteristics is complex and difficult and cannot be fully understood without in-depth research. The issues we have discussed here will give you an introduction to the problems but you need to continue reading and exploring these issues to fully comprehend their implications. One topic to consider for continued discussion would be how these social problems relate to the future stability of these countries.

Keywords: Estonia, Latvia, Lithuania, Russia, social characteristics, divorce, marriage, abortion, suicide

Part Six

Activities
for *Latin America*
and the Caribbean
Using Encarta®
Virtual Globe

Where *Not* to Be in Raincoat Sales: High and Dry in the Atacama Desert

The Atacama Desert of northern Chile is one of the driest places on the planet because of its combination of sub-tropical high pressure and cold water upwelling associated with the Peru Current. Some locations in the 600-mile long desert region such as Calama have never recorded any rainfall at all! But how do humans cope with the nearly non-existent precipitation and why would they want to live there anyway? Let's start to answer this question by locating our study area. Use the *Find* icon to create a map of the Atacama Desert. Click on *Antofagasta* and select *Geography* to read about economic characteristics of the area and why anyone would choose to reside in a region that receives 0.5 inches of precipitation per year. Mining is a major activity in the Atacama. Just north of Calama is the mining town of Chuquicamata. Use *Find* to locate *Calama*. Move your cursor and click on *Chuquicamata.* Then select *Sights & Sounds* to see why Chile is one of the world's major mineral producers. What do you suppose might be the environmental and social costs for this type of resource exploitation?

Now, move back to the main map of the Atacama Desert. Then, select *Sights & Sounds* and take a peek at the *Atacama Desert Rings*. Could this location be featured on the next episode of the *X-Files* as proof-positive of alien contact? This bizarre looking landscape doesn't offer too much in the way of human habitation, but from it you can learn much about the biogeography of the Atacama plateau. Would you expect the Atacama to experience such low temperatures allowing for these types of formations? Now select *Web Links* and click on *Plants of the Atacama Desert.* Why do ecologists describe Lomas Formations as fog oases? What is phytogeography and how can it be used to interpret environments and climate in the Atacama and elsewhere? Compare the survival strategies developed by desert vegetation to those used by humans as described in *Water Innovations in the Atacama Desert* Web page. Would it be safe to say that in this case for those adapting to the harsh realities of the Atacama, it's a good thing to be in a fog?

Keywords: Atacama Desert, Chile, Mining, Climate, Biogeography

Trail of Years:
Historical Linkages Along
The Inca Highway

Much like the Romans centuries before, the Inca
developed an extensive empire in Andean America.
Military power, food production, and distribution
were made possible by, and supported through, an
amazing transportation network high in the Andes
Mountains. How did they do it? Through the *mita*
labor system, males were conscripted to work a
portion of the year in the military or on such public
works projects as road building. The map in your
textbook on page 53 (Figure 3.2) provides insight as
to the extent of the highway network. Imagine the
difficulty of carving and maintaining a roadway in
such high altitudes, subject to adverse weather
conditions, using 15th and 16th century technology.
Then there was always the risk of a fourteen-llama
pileup on the Cuzco throughway!

Let's start our journey on the Inca highway at Cuzco
(also spelled Cusco), centrally located along the
transportation network. Use *Find* to create a map of
Cuzco and the surrounding area. Click on
Geography to get a feel for the history and physical
setting of the city. How does the name of the city
itself reflect its significance to the Inca Empire?
Now take a virtual tour of the city by selecting *Sights*

& Sounds. What cultural clues can you gain from this series of slides and narratives that illustrate the confluence of indigenous and colonial cultures? Listen to the Bolivian panpipe music. How have the Quechua- and Aymara-speaking peoples retained their language and music traditions when indigenous peoples elsewhere have struggled to maintain their cultural identities? How do you think the diffusion of Incan culture, as well as that of the Spanish, was influenced by the transportation network? Compare the map on page 86 (Figure 3.7) with that of the Inca highway map on page 53. How did colonials adapt the Inca transportation network to suit their own needs?

Along the trail is one of the most famous Incan ruins, Machu Picchu (also spelled Machupicchu). Today, tourists usually launch their trek to the ancient ruins from the city of Cuzco. To get a better understanding of the site and its relationship to the Inca trail, go to *Web Links* and select the *Machu Picchu* site. While navigating through the page, click on the *Inca Trail* link identified within the text. Would you walk that many miles for a llama?

Keywords: Inca, Machu Picchu, Cuzco, transportation, Andes Mountains, diffusion

Coca Puffs: Cracking Down on the Cocaine Trade

Without a doubt the most profitable agricultural products for some Latin American countries are also highly illegal in most places. The illicit drug trade between Columbia and the United States has been well documented and has been a source of friction between the two countries. Americans have encouraged farmers to grow alternative crops such as cut flowers, another high-value yet much more acceptable export product.

While Colombia is a major cocaine refiner, it is not the leading producer of coca. This distinction rests with Peru. Peru is the world's leading producer of coca leaves. Using the *Find Places* tool, create a map of Peru. Click on *Society* and go to the section on *Infrastructure*. For additional information on Peru, go to *Web Links* and review the *U.S. State Department Travel Advisory* page. From what you have read, what factors contribute to the drug trade in Peru and do you think this will continue as a chronic problem? Next, let's compare conditions in Peru to those in Colombia.

Locate Colombia by using the *Find* option. For an overview of the country's economy, click on *Society*, and then *Economy* for background statistics and descriptions of agriculture. Colombia produces a wide variety of crops thanks to varied topography, soils, and climate. Consuming coca leaves, in a variety of forms, is an ancient tradition. Yet coca plays a central role in the contemporary illegal drug trade in the U.S. and elsewhere. Return to the map of Colombia and continue to explore this issue using the *Web Links*. Select, *Colombia--A Country Study*, then scan down the list and click on *Drugs and Society*. Read through the narrative keeping in mind how the geography of Colombia has played a key role in the illegal drug trade. What crop became popular to produce for urbanites by the 1930s and what were the results of its expansion? How does drug crop cultivation affect food production? How did the cocaine trade develop in Colombia? What were the early connections between Colombia, Cuba, Chile, and the United States? What were the societal consequences of the drug trade in Colombia? What is basuco and how has it lead to serious problems in Colombia?

Based on what you now know, do you think there are any solutions to the drug problems within Colombia? How would these solutions be similar or different from solving the global drug trade dilemma?

Keywords: Peru, Colombia, coca, cocaine, illegal drug trade, marijuana, *basuco*

Why You Have to Go to New York City to Get Your Go-Go Boots Shined: Brazilians on the Move

The mobility of Brazilians has changed the demographics within the country as well as in regions well beyond its political boundaries. The overwhelming trend in Brazil over the past century has been for rural migrants to seek their fortunes in urban areas. This has lead to spectacular urban population growth rates far exceeding their rates of natural increase. Brazil has also been a source of emigrants. So what exactly do Brazilian migration and go-go boots have in common? Let's go to *Encarta* and find out.

First, create a map of Brazil using the *Find Places* tool. Select *Society* and read the sections on *Demographics* and *Infrastructure*. Brazil has welcomed many immigrants to it's shores as well. What are the major ethnic groups in Brazil? Which Asian nationality is well represented in Brazil and where do they live? Where would you find the largest African Brazilian population concentrations? How has migration within Brazil changed the lives of indigenous peoples such as the Yanomami?

Next, let's switch to *Web Links* and click on *Brazzil*.
When the homepage for this on-line Brazilian culture
magazine comes up, select *Search* and enter the word
migration. You should get a table of at least 14
articles with a focus on migration. Read the
following articles selected from the table and answer
the corresponding questions.

New Gold Rush in Serra Pelada

Where is Serra Pelada (you can use the *Find Places*
tool to locate it on the map) and why would 80,000
migrants want to go there? What are the conditions
in the mining camps in Serra Pelada? Have men and
women had equal opportunities to make their
fortunes?

American Workers, Exiles, and Emigrants in Brazil

What is *jeitinho brasileiro* and why might it be more
important for Americans to grasp than Portuguese?
Why do most Americans immigrate to Brazil? When
did this pattern of migration begin and where was the
major destination? What are some of the cultural
adjustments to be made by American expatriates?

Favelas Commemorate 100 Years

What is a favela and why would few Brazilians
enthusiastically celebrate this special anniversary?
How did the favelas get their name and who is
"credited" with establishing them?
Who lives in favelas and how does their standard of
living compare to other urban dwellers? What is
Rochina's claim to fame? Why are the favelas of Rio
de Janeiro situated on hills? What did urban planners

have in mind for favelas over the years? What types of social class rivalries have developed between favelas?

News From Brazil-Brazilian Emigration March 96
Prior to the 1960s, where were the source regions for immigrants to Brazil? What happened in the 1960s to change that pattern? Why do you think Brazilians are leaving the country in the 1990s? Where are Brazilians choosing to live in the United States? How has chain migration reinforced the pattern of Brazilian settlement in the United States? What are the occupational and educational differences between male and female Brazilian immigrants? What types of acculturation problems do Brazilian expatriates encounter in their adopted homelands? What is life like for an illegal Brazilian immigrant in the U.S.? Why are some Brazilians moving to Japan? How are their experiences different or similar to those who chose the U.S.? Why would Brazilians seek political asylum in Great Britain? Why does Florida lead in the numbers of Brazilians behind bars? Who are the *Brazucas* and where is "Little Brazil?"

And after reading this final article, you now know why NewYork City, shoe shines, go-go boots and *Brazucas* go together!

Keywords: Brazil, migration, immigration, emigration, favelas

Show Some Spine! Land Use in the Latin American City

As shown in Figure 6-6 (p. 177) of the textbook, the land use structure of Latin American cities is quite different from that typically found in cities of North America or Europe. In North America the poorest people often live in inner city neighborhoods fairly close to the downtown or central business district (CBD). By the same token, rich people often live at the periphery of the city in large houses on estate-sized lots. This leads to a fundamental paradox: poor people living on very expensive centrally located urban land and wealthy people living on relatively inexpensive land at the periphery. This paradox has led one urban scholar to suggest that in North America, accessibility to central places must be an inferior good while quantity of land itself must be a superior good. What are inferior and superior goods? Think of steak and potatoes. Generally speaking, as the income of a person rises his or her propensity to eat steak increases (especially some of the tenderest, juiciest cuts). Likewise, as a person's income rises, his or her propensity to eat potatoes, a cheap source of starch and calories in the diet, tends to decrease. We say that steak is a superior good, whose consumption increases with increasing income, whereas potatoes are an inferior good whose consumption decreases with increasing income. Can you think of other examples of superior and inferior goods?

Latin American cities (and cities throughout third world countries for that matter) do not manifest this paradox. In Latin America, the wealthy often live in central locations in residential districts close to shops and services of all kinds. Alternatively, the poor are forced to live on marginal land at the periphery of the city often in slum-like conditions. These areas are known by a variety of terms in Latin America— favelas in Brazil, poblaciones caiampas ("mushroom settlements") in Chile and, more generally, squatter slums elsewhere. Using the *Find Places* command, type in *Mexico City*. Now click on the sidebar entitled *Sights and Sounds* and read the caption on the slide designated *Urban Hardships*. These marginal areas are often, surprisingly, slums of hope rather than of despair. As bad as conditions are in these places that often lack basic services such as sewage treatment and piped potable water supplies, they are often better than the conditions in the rural countryside from which many of these recent immigrants arrive.

The Griffin-Ford model accounts for changes in these squatter slums. Eventually, through the dint of effort of their residents, these shantytowns are upgraded— the tarpaper shack gets siding, a new roof, an inside toilet, and piped water. This is called "in-situ accretion" in the model. Whole neighborhoods slowly become less tenuous and more permanent in their characteristics until a point is reached in which it is difficult to tell that the area was ever a peripheral slum area. In the Latin American city, accessibility to the central area is a superior good. Rich residential areas such as the Polonco district in Mexico City are close to the Zona Rosa, a major shopping district in downtown Mexico City and not far from the green and leafy Chapultepec Park. Using the *Find* command, select *Mexico City*. Then bring up a map of the city's street layout and general configuration. Do you see Chapultepec Park? How close is it to the main square (the Zócolo)? Hint: One of the buildings on the Zócolo is the National Palace (the Palacio National). Like many of the Law of the Indies towns, Mexico City's true heart is the main square (the Zócolo) not far from the center of the ancient Aztec capital Tenóchtitlan, from which modern Mexico City grew.

If the Zócolo is the cultural and governmental center of Mexico City, where is "the affluent spine" of the Griffin-Ford model? Most likely it would be a broad avenue that leads away from the Zócolo. Click on *Sights and Sounds* and choose the *Satellite View of Mexico City*. Is the avenue on which the main entrance to Chapultepec Park is located part of the affluent spine? How about the diagonal avenue trending northeast of the Zócolo (i.e., La Avenida de los Insurgentes)? Would it also be a continuation of the affluent spine? Why or why not?

Keywords: affluent spine, in situ accretion, squatter slums, Mexico City, Griffin-Ford model

The Tin Men and Women: Mining in Bolivia

Since the 1860s, Bolivia has been a major source of tin. The story of tin and other mineral extraction in Bolivia is as much a geologic story as it is one of politics, economics, and culture. Let's dig deep into Bolivian mining beginning with a general overview of the country's geography and economy. Create a map of Bolivia using the *Find Places* tool. Click on *Land and Climate* for a quick overview of Bolivia's physical geography. Next, select *Fact and Figures* and then *Society* to read the *Infrastructure* section. Based on what you have read, what basic factors have contributed to the chronic economic development problems in Bolivia? How have natural resources been exploited in the country? What types of minerals are extracted and where are the primary markets?

Now let's take a closer look at the mining industry in Bolivia. Go to *Web Links* and click on *Bolivia--A Country Study*. This site has an extensive collection of information on all aspects of Bolivia. To focus our attention on the mining industry, use the *Search* tool at the top of the web page and enter *mining*. Your search results should appear as a list of dozens of links the first of which is titled *Mining*. Click on *Mining* and view the two slides and read the accompanying material. How would you describe the miners depicted in the photographs? What are they extracting and what type of technology is being employed?

Now go back to the mining page and select *Structure of the Mining Industry*. What is "Comibol" and why was it created? How were "medium" and "small" miners along with cooperatives and others, able to out-produce Comibol by the late 1980s?

Return to the mining page and click on *Tin and Related Metals*. After reading this section, how would you describe the changes in the Bolivian tin industry in the past 100 years? What types of structural problems within the tin industry exerted political pressure on the Bolivian government? How did the government respond to the collapse of tin prices? Which minerals have supplanted tin as the country's main mining focus? Where are the markets for Bolivian minerals?

Finally, go back to the mining page and select *The Liberal Party and the Rise of Tin* for a more in-depth discussion of mining and politics. Review this section and answer the following questions"
• How did the rise of the Liberal Party relate to the tin industry?
• Why did the Liberals think it was a sweet idea to move the capital to La Paz? How did these same Liberals intervene in boundary disputes between Bolivia and its neighbors?
• How did the development of transportation infrastructure by the Liberals and conditions in Europe affect the tin industry?

- How were indigenous peasants affected by the mining industry?
- What do you think the future holds for Bolivia and how is its political and economic stability tied to the mining industry?

Keywords: Bolivia, mining, tin, politics, Comibol, Liberals, trade

Yúcatan If You Don't Wear Sunscreen: Tourism in the Land of the Maya

One of the facts that many people find amazing about Mexico and Central America is that there are still living descendants of the ancient Maya living all the way from the Yúcatan peninsula to the Central American countries of Guatemala, Honduras, and Belize. There may be as many as four million Maya living in the Yúcatan area alone. The Caribbean coast of Mexico including the Mexican states of Yúcatan and Quintana Roo has become a major tourist destination in the past few decades. Tourism has surpassed petroleum as the largest earner of income in Mexico. In fact former President Portillo of Mexico was heavily involved in the development of the Caribbean coast which has become the engine of economic development of the region. The ripple effect of tourism is even felt in the state capital of Mérida, hundreds of miles from the coastal development. Many of the locations along Mexico's Caribbean coast, especially Cancún and Cozumel, have been targeted to U.S. tourists. The tourist experience is a multi-faceted one. In this land of the Maya ruin, do you think that the cultural history of the region is foremost in the mind of the tourist or does it merely provide a scenic backdrop and/or diversionary side trip for the sun and fun pleasure seeker? Let's see by taking a virtual tour of the

291

Cozumel-Cancún area. Click on *Find* and then *Places* and type in *Cozumel*. Which of these two popular destinations is on an island? What other island is nearby that is also a tourist destination, albeit mainly for Mexicans themselves? Now type in *Cancún* because there are associated *Web Links* with that place name. Click on the Web site entitled *Cancún On-line*. You will notice a choice called *Tours from Cancún*. Let's see what they recommend. Interestingly, two of the three most highly recommended tours involve travel to ancient Maya sites—Chichen Itza and Tulúm. So, let's go! Click on *Chichen Itza*. The text suggests that it was the capital of the Mayan Empire. In fact, it was the capital of the highland Maya, a group whose Classic Period came a bit later than the lowland Maya located further south. What forms the "serpent" Kukulcan on the side of the main pyramid? When does the "serpent" appear? Is this evidence that the ancient Maya were knowledgeable of astronomy? Why or why not?

Now click on *Isla Mujeres*. How does this translate into English? When was it founded and by whom? Now, let's tour *Cozumel Island*. What national park is located on the island? What do tourists like to do there? The last highly recommended trip is to *Tulúm*. Tulúm is built on a cliff. Many archaeologists think that its most famous structure—El Castillo was used as a lighthouse to warn nearby canoes and ships about the dangerous shoals and reefs in the waters. Nearby is *Xel-Ha*. How is it described? How do you think that Mayan royalty explored undersea life?

A closer examination of both Cozumel and Tulúm can be found by clicking on the area marked *Read this before exploring the site*. Click on *Cozumel* and answer the following questions. Are there Mayan sites on the island of Cozumel? From what period do the ruins at San Gervasion date? The ruin was evidently built to honor Ixchel. Who or what is Ixchel? On the south part of the island is a small ruin called Tumba del Caracoal. How does that translate into English?

Now click on *Tulúm* and examine the sites available there. Two are private commercial developments. What exactly can one find and do at Xcaret? What about Xen-He? The photographs look beautiful. What is a deep natural well in this area called? Many of these wells were sacred to the Maya. Some were even used to dispose of the victims of human sacrifice, but let's go on to more pleasant subjects. Let's take the 100-mile Cancún-to-Tulúm trip as described by travel writer Katharine Hyde. How old is Cancún as a resort? Does this surprise you? We learn that thanks "to the sensitivity of many developers" there are still miles of unspoiled beauty along the shore of the Cancún to Tulúm corridor. What is a green angel? What appears to be the speed limit along Highway 307 between Cancún and Tulúm? Approximately 20 miles south of the airport servicing Cancún is Croco Cun. What is it famous for? What is the importance of Puerto Morelos to the state of Quintana Roo? What will you find at the Dr. Alfredo Barrera Marine Botanical Garden? Where is a quiet spot where you can comb the beach for shells? What former sleepy fishing village is now a thriving tourist town? What did the Maya call it? Where was the departure point for Maya pilgrims to cross the water to the sacred isle of Cozumel? If you go snorkeling at Paamul, what do you have to watch out for? Can you get to the small Maya ruin at Xaac by land or by boat? How then, do you get there? What is the meaning of Akumal? Why are fewer sea turtles laying their eggs there than in years past? Where does Ms. Hyde, the writer of this article, suggest is "almost the perfect beach"?

So, did this virtual tour whet your appetite for the Mexican Caribbean coast? Do you think that becoming informed about the rudiments of classic Maya culture would add to the enjoyment of a vacation there? Will the Maya ruins serve as focal point or backdrop to your vacation to the Mexican Caribbean coast?

Keywords: tourism, Cozumel, Cancún, Tulúm, Maya, Yúcatan Peninsula

Roller Costa Rica: Riding the Wave of Prosperity

When we think of a Central American country, we often have a stereotype of a banana republic (not the store in the mall) which destroys native species of plants and animals to make room for export-oriented plantation agriculture. We think of countries that are subject to periodic takeovers by military juntas and citizens with little freedom of speech or assembly.

We are unlikely to think about a country with a growing and prosperous middle class, an enviable government, or one with environmental protections plans for endangered species of flora and fauna. Welcome to Costa Rica. It is indeed a rich coast as the name implies in Spanish and a rich contrast to some of its more beleaguered neighbors (e.g., Guatemala, El Salvador, Nicaragua) that have suffered and still suffer the atrocities of civil strife and violence. It was former Costa Rican President Oscar Arias Sanchez who brokered the end to the civil strife in Nicaragua and won the Nobel Peace Prize in 1987. Transitions of government, mandated every four years, have been remarkably peaceful even when the party in power loses the next election. You can probably imagine why, when choosing among Central American countries, many transnational corporations choose to set up shop and do business in this stable and peaceful country.

Let's learn more about this fascinating country by clicking on *Find* and then *Places* and typing *Costa Rica*. What physical feature strikes you about Costa Rica? How large is Costa Rica compared to Guatemala? In order to find out, click on the sidebar marked *Land and Climate*. What are the names of the three mountain ranges that appear to dominate such a large portion of the landscape? Do these mountain ranges contain active volcanoes? If so, name one. What is the name of the most fertile plateau in the country where much of the commercial agriculture takes place? Where within Costa Rica is the average temperature the hottest? Where is it the coolest? When does the rainy season normally begin and how long does it usually last?

Now click on the sidebar entitled *Facts and Figures* for a thumbnail sketch of the country, basic statistics on the health, education and welfare of its citizenry and its economy. The capital of San Jose accounts for at least 22 percent of the entire country's population? Is San Jose a primate city (i.e., is its population considerably more than twice the next largest city in the country)? How do you think Costa Rica's life expectancies compare with other countries of Central and South America? How do they compare with those of the United States? How do you account for this when the average income of the country would place it in the third world category (i.e., $1,774 gross domestic product per capital)? Although derogatorily referred to as a "banana republic", whose terms of foreign trade were once controlled by the United Fruit Company, what is

Costa Rica's main export today? Would the
country's literacy rate be an attraction to the typical
transnational corporation? Why or why not?

Now click on the sidebar entitled *Society* for a closer
look at language and customs of the people. Why are
the Costa Rican people called Ticos? Do you think
that Costa Rica's high marriage rate has anything to
do with the dominant religion of the country? Why
or why not? What would you be eating if you were
served a national favorite lengua en salsa? How
about mondongo? When might the title Doña be
given preference over the title Señora? Why are the
beaches especially crowded between January and
April? What proportion of the land in this small
country has been set aside for nature reserves and
national parks? What holiday takes place on April
11th? Who is Rivas? Who is Walker? Who is Juan
Santamaria? Who was elected president of the
country in 1948 when the current string of stable
democratic governments began? Did he serve the
country as president after his initial term? If so,
when? Where does most of the electricity to supply
the industries and cities of the country come from?
How does Costa Rica's infant mortality rate of 16 per
1,000 live births, the lowest in Central and South
America, compare with the same statistic for the
United States? What about the same comparison
with Canada?

Now click on the sidebar called *Sights and Sounds*.
On the slide entitled *Rich Farmland in Costa Rica*
what does the caption say are the two large areas of
rich volcanic soil where much of the commercial

agriculture takes place? Now take a look at *Costa Rican Coffee Plants*. Where are most of the coffee plants grown? If coffee beans are brownish-black in color, why are the berries from which they are derived bright red? Finally, focus on *Valuable Crop*. Why do you think the bananas are wrapped in plastic? What percentage of Costa Rica's workers are farmers?

To learn a bit more about the early history of banana plantations in Costa Rica, click onto the sidebar marked *Web Links* and then on the link called Encarta Online--Costa Rica. Now scroll down that material to the section marked *Agriculture*. In what part of Costa Rica was the world's largest banana plantation developed? What company developed it? What two port cities were developed by that company to ship bananas to world markets? Why do you think that bananas are not raised in the rich and fertile highlands region of the country?

Keywords: Costa Rica, bananas, coffee, democracy, stable government

Volcanoes in the Lesser Antilles: Hot Times in the Islands

The Caribbean. Mention that geographic location and images of sunny vacations, secluded beaches, cultural diversity, and exotic settings spring to mind. What should also appear in your mental slide show are the inherent hazards of living in the Caribbean realm, such as hurricanes and volcanoes. Hurricanes come and go and strike mercurially throughout the region but volcanoes are more of a permanent fixture on the landscape. Volcanoes formed many islands in the Caribbean and continue their work of creation and destruction. Situated on the Caribbean Plate, tectonic activity in the region continues to shape the physical geography and daily lives of island dwellers.

To explore the breathtakingly beautiful but equally deadly volcanic landscapes of the Caribbean, begin by creating a map of *Guadeloupe*, site of the first observed eruption in the *West Indies*. Go to *Web Sites* and click on *Soufriere Volcano*. The map on this page illustrates the locations of volcanoes in the *Lesser Antilles* volcanic arc and provides a good reference point for our tour. Take a look at the photo of La Soufriere and read the accompanying description. Keeping in mind the conditions in Guadeloupe, go to the *Volcano World* link at the bottom of the page and click on the icon. When the *Volcano World* Web page comes up, use the search engine and type *Caribbean*. The results of your search should yield a list of volcano Web sites in the Caribbean. From this list you will be able to take a virtual tour of volcanoes in the region. Select each of the following sites and answer the corresponding questions:

Dominica, West Indies Location
• How do you think the "Valley of Desolation" got its name?
• Use *Find Places* and create a map of *Dominica* in Encarta and click on *Land and Climate*. Why does the United Nations consider this island one the most "disaster-prone countries in the world?" Is it because of volcanoes?

Mt. Pelee, Martinique, Caribbean
• Why is this volcano described as "notorious?"
• How did Mt. Pelee get its name?
• Why is the city of St. Pierre in such a dangerous location?
• What is *nuees ardentes*?

Soufriere, St. Vincent, West Indies Location
• Why is *this* "Soufriere" considered to be more dangerous than the volcano of the same name in Guadeloupe?

Kick-'em Jenny, West Indies Location
• Other than it's unusual name, what makes Kick-em Jenny so different from other volcanoes in the Lesser Antilles arc?
• Which two tectonic plates are involved in the creation of this volcano?

An Old Volcano Awakens on Montserrat

• This account was written prior to the major eruptions in 1997 that brought death and destruction to residents surrounding the Soufriere Hills in Montserrat. For a look at Montserrat after the major eruptions occurred, go back to Encarta and use *Find Places* to create a map of *Montserrat*. Click on *Web Links* and select *Soufriere Hills Volcano* and *Volcano World: Soufriere Hills*. On the *Soufriere Hills Volcano* page, be sure to click on *Government of Montserrat* and *Montserrat Volcano Observatory* as well as the links for images.

• What types of landform features a result of the Soufriere Hills eruption?

• How has the British government responded to the emergency situation on Montserrat?

• How did Hurricane Erika and the volcano combine to form additional hazards for the region?

• What has happened to the town of Plymouth as a result of the eruptions?

For each of the previously mentioned locations, you can expand your tour by creating a map of each island and selecting *Land and Climate* and *Sights and Sounds*. There are mountains of information that flow out of these sources.

Keywords: Caribbean, Lesser Antilles, volcanic arc, plate tectonics, volcanoes, hazards, Guadeloupe, Dominica, Martinique, Montserrat, nuees ardentes

Mountains of Potatoes: The Nature and Cultures of the Andes

The Andes Mountains extend for over 5,000 miles from the Caribbean in the north to Tierra del Fuego at the southernmost tip of the South American continent. Along its course, the Andes cut across cultural, physical, and political regions, creating a barrier between the narrow Pacific coastal region and the bulk of the continent. We will review several countries within the Andes region including Colombia, Ecuador, Peru, and Bolivia, and discuss their differences and similarities. Then we will change the scale of our investigation by making a side-trip to the Altiplano and Lake Titicaca.

Begin by creating a map of the Andes Mountains by using the *Find Places* tool. Read the description of the physical environment by clicking on *Geography* and then take a look at the slides in *Sights and Sounds*. What are some of the challenges faced by those who live in the Andes?

For more detailed information on Andean countries, switch to *Web Links* and click on *A Guide to the Andean Countries*. Check out each of the links under *Contents* and read the short narratives for Colombia, Ecuador, Peru, and Bolivia. After reading about the physical environment, what are some of the more unique aspects of the Andes? How has elevation played a role in the diversity of Andean flora and fauna? How did the colonial period impact indigenous peoples of the Andes? How did the demand for labor and migration during the colonial era influence disease diffusion?

Now that you have read a little about each of the four selected Andean countries, you might be able to answer more questions than you think. Which is the only South American country with ports on both the Pacific Ocean and Caribbean Sea? Which is the smallest of the Andean countries? Which Andean country has the highest percentage of indigenous populations?

Which of the Andean countries is largest in area and borders all other Andean states? Which is the only landlocked Andean country? Which of these countries is the most urban? Which has the highest gross national product?

Now that you have some background information on the Andes region, let's take a closer look at one location in particular, Lake Titicaca. Go to a map of *Lake Titicaca* (Lago Titicaca) using the *Find Places* option. Click on *Geography*. How does the lake influence the local climate? How has Lake Titicaca influenced local cultures? You can view an example of local culture by selecting *Sights and Sounds* and viewing the slide titled *Uru of Lago Titicaca*. Now go to *Web Links* and click on the *Aymara Culture*. Read through this material. You can learn more about these indigenous peoples by using *Find Places* to create a map of *Bolivia* and selecting the *Web Link* titled *Aymara Page*. Based on what you have read in these two web sites, what do you think are the most important historical events that changed the Aymaran way of life? What crops are generally raised in the Lake Titicaca region and why has the potato figured so prominently in this region? What does the future hold for the Aymara and other indigenous groups in the Andes?

Keywords: Andes Mountains, Colombia, Ecuador, Peru, Bolivia, Lake Titicaca, Aymara

Were They Brazil Nuts? Brasilia in Retrospect

It's been said that the history of the United States can be summed up in its frontier mentality—that strong desire (or manifest destiny if you prefer) to establish the country from sea to shining sea. Depending on which historian you read, that task was accomplished at the very latest by the first decade of the 20th century.

Brazil's sense of manifest destiny is much more recent. Theirs is a great push inward from the large and important coastal cities of Rio de Janeiro and São Paulo into the rich and largely untapped interior of the Mato Grosso and Amazon regions.

One of the symbols of this inward turning was the movement of the capital city from coastal Rio de Janeiro to Brasilia some 750 miles into the interior of the country. At first, members of the Brazilian parliament, used to the nightlife of cosmopolitan Rio de Janeiro, were reticent to stay in Brasilia on the weekends. Once weekday business concluded, parliamentary members would fly the 750 miles back to the glamour of the former capital, leaving Brasilia a ghost town. Let's find out more about Brasilia and how it might have changed since those early days as the new capital. Click on *Find a Place* and type *Brasilia*. Study the relative location of Brasilia and then click on the sidebar entitled *Geography* and answer the following questions: What is the approximate population of Brasilia? Is the city located in a tropical rainforest? Is it located in the Amazon region? When did Brasilia become the capital of Brazil? Who was the main force behind the move to the interior that had been suggested ever since 1789? What were the primary reasons for siting the capital and the federal district (Districo Federal) where they are? What architect developed the overall plan for the city of Brasilia? What is Brasilia's layout said to resemble? Who designed most of the public buildings? What large river runs nearby the city?

Now turn to *Sights and Sounds* and examine the caption and slide called *Modern Architecture in Brasilia*. How would you describe the setting for the formal government buildings? Does the city look lively and inviting? Why or why not? Let's explore the architecture of the city in greater detail by clicking on the *Web Links* and going to the site entitled *Architecture of Brasilia*. From what existing state or states was the Districto Federal carved out? Who was the landscape architect who designed the green spaces, parks and formal gardens? Look at the image of the *Ministerial Esplanade*. What is your impression of that "public space"? Now look at the *Metropolitan Cathedral*. What is the shape of the building supposed to represent? What do you suppose the statuary in front of the building symbolizes? Finally, take a look at *A Plan of the City*. Is the plane that the grand plan is supposed to resemble readily apparent?

Now let's explore another of the *Web Links* for Brasilia. Click on the site entitled *Brasilia's Homepage*. According to the information provided there, what was to be the maximum population of the city according to the planners who developed the master plan (Plan Piloto)? Are the satellite communities needed to house the workers outside of the master plan area really favelas (squatter slums)? Why or why not? What are the four different meanings attached to the term "Brasilia"? Using the most generous definition, how many people are there in Brasilia? What is wrong with the myth that the city is completely automobile-oriented, a city of wide-open spaces and broad streets? Can you briefly summarize the status of Brasilia as the capital city around 1964, the time of the military coup and four years after it had been officially declared the capital? Was there a real movement afoot to move the capital back to Rio de Janeiro? Finally, do the legislators still spend as little time as possible in Brasilia, returning instead the 741 air miles to Rio de Janeiro at every opportunity? What would you do if you were a Brazilian politician?

Keywords: Brasilia, Rio de Janeiro, Brazil, President Juscelino Kubitschek

Don't Cry For Me Argentina: You Can't Be Pompous About the Pampas

The rich grasslands of the Pampas of Argentina are the home of the South American cowboy called the gaucho. There are colorful stories of gauchos not only rounding up and branding cattle, but also capturing with their bolos the swift and large flightless birds of the Pampas called the rhea. The bolo is best described as a cross between a lasso and a slingshot. Wooden balls encased in leather are used for weights and the bola is thrown at the feet of the rhea (or more likely the calf about to be branded) to wrap around them and trip the animal to the ground. Unlike the lasso of the cowboy, once the bola of the gaucho has been released, it must hit its target or be retrieved. Afterwards, the gauchos sit around the campfire sipping yerba maté, a kind of tea popular in the region, through silver sipping straws placed into gourds that serve as cups. At least that is the romantic image of the gaucho and this rich grassland region. What is the reality? Let's find out by exploring *Encarta Virtual Globe*. Click on *Find a Place* and type in *Pampas, Argentina*. What does the term pampas mean? From what language is the phrase derived? What are the two parts of the Pampas? Can you think of any other grassland areas that might be similarly divided between humid and semi-arid? What about the Corn Belt of the United States (the humid grassland) and the wheat country of the Great Plains (the semi-arid grassland)? How apt is that analogy? Are the Pampas of Argentina the only pampas in South America? Now click on *Sights and Sounds* and bring up the image entitled *Herding Cattle on the Pampas*. Are you disappointed to find that the modern-day gaucho is just as likely to use a truck for a cattle roundup as a horse?

Using the *Find* and *Countries* pull-down menus, type in *Argentina* and let's see what else we can find out about this country that contains the Pampas. Click on the sidebar called *Land and Climate* and read the material contained there. The rich and fertile Pampas appear to be a product of erosion and deposition. What type(s) of erosion predominate? What is the source area of the deposited material? The Pampas are very large. They extend almost 1,600 kilometers from north to south. What subtropical physical area lies immediately to the north of the temperate Pampas? If the Pampas are so rich and the metropolitan area of Buenos Aires is so large (containing more than ten million of the country's 32-plus million people), why is Argentina one of the least densely populated countries in the world? Why do you suppose that per capita agricultural production has declined since 1980 despite very slow population growth in the country?

Now click on the sidebar marked *Society* for more insights into the Argentine situation. When was divorce legalized in Argentina? Why do you think it came so late in the country's history? What do

Argentines eat more of on a per capita basis than any other people on earth? Why would street vendors of food products have a tough time making a living in Buenos Aires? What is considered the country's national sport? Being a nominally Catholic country, Holy Week events are important holidays. What does Maundy Thursday mean? What event is celebrated the day after April Fool's Day? What do Argentines call the Falkland Islands? What does the feast of the Immaculate Conception on December 8th celebrate? At what age is a girl's childhood said to end? How is this rite of passage to womanhood celebrated? A new form of singing evolved from the folk ballad and nationalistic and political themes. What is this form of music called? For a sample of what such a song sounds like, click on *Sights and Sounds* and then on the slide entitled *Historic Plaza*. Who is the singer? What are the origins of Argentina's national dance--the tango? Would you classify the origins as "highbrow"?

What famous president of Argentina was overthrown in 1955 only to be returned from exile and to political power in 1973? What was the name of his second wife (Hint: look at the title of this unit and think Madonna or Patty Lupone). This president's third wife was declared Vice President in 1973 and succeeded him as President when he died the next year. Who was she? What was the name of the Marxist guerrilla uprising that prompted the military to take over the government in 1976? What is the "Dirty War"? Who are the "disappeared"?

Who is now the president of Argentina and how many times has he been re-elected since first coming to office in 1991? What is his family's ethnic background? Who was the chief architect of economic reform that brought inflation down from its annual growth of 4000 percent? When Argentina once again suffered recession and high unemployment in 1996 what happened to Dominic Cavallo? If you worked in Argentina do you think you would enjoy an aquinaldo?

Keywords: Pampas, gaucho, Argentina, Perón, Falkland Islands (Islas Malvinas)

Banking on the Future of Latin America: Solving Rural Poverty

One of the major challenges facing Latin America at the close of the 20th century is balancing urban and rural development. Many cities such as São Paulo, Brazil, and Mexico City, Mexico, have experienced explosive growth in the post-World War II years but with serious social and economic consequences. A substantial portion of the growing urban populations originated from the rural hinterlands and generally lack marketable skills and financial resources. What are some of the consequences of such uneven growth? The World Bank has examined the rural development issue and considers it to be a serious challenge to Latin American stability as well as a factor that inhibits the region's participation in the global economy.

You can read about Latin America through the eyes of the World Bank by accessing their web site. To do this, create a map of *South America* and select *Web Links* and click on *The World Bank Latin American and Caribbean Technical Department*. Select the language in which you want to read the material and move on to the introductory page. The first site to visit is *Agriculture, Natural Resource Management, and Rural Poverty*. Read the papers listed here: "The Plundering of Agriculture in Developing Countries," "Rural Poverty in Latin America and the

Caribbean," and "Determinants of Rural Poverty: A Quantitative Analysis." Based on what you have learned from these three research papers, you can answer the following questions:

How are urban and rural development related to environmental issues? What are the global implications?

Why is poverty in Latin America generalized as an "urban problem?" What does the future hold for Latin American "smallholders" or *minifundistas*? Why do urban poverty rates appear to be increasing while rural poverty remains fairly constant? How do education and household characteristics influence economic status in rural areas? Why does the World Bank interpret rural poverty in Latin America differently from other world regions? How have the legacies of colonialism translated into rural poverty for indigenous peoples? Why have governments failed to address poverty associated with subsistence agriculture? Why are the rural poor of Latin America in a less favorable position for off-farm employment than their counterparts in Asia?

Why does the World Bank now frown upon large government programs aimed at relieving poverty? How have tariffs on imports and exports as well as internal tax structures affected economic development in rural areas of Latin America?

Rural and urban poverty in Latin America is widespread and difficult to mitigate. While government programs vary from country to country,

313

the overall picture remains constant--rural to urban migration, lack of government focus on poverty issues, and issues related to land tenure continue to complicate regional economic stability. If you were hired by the World Bank to address these issues, what would you choose as your main agenda?

Keywords: Latin America, World Bank, rural development, poverty, agriculture, land tenure

The Index
A Volume-by-Volume Cross-referencing Guide

This section is designed to help both the instructor and student find related material in books other than the one assigned as a textbook for the course. We hope you will find this cross-referencing effort useful. We assume that you will be examining, if not always assigning, every activity associated with the textbook that you have adopted. Since these activities were designed to stand alone from the textbooks and all use *Encarta Virtual Globe*, the instructor can find and use an activity that is not keyed to the particular textbook that he or she is using. These activities can be used for a variety of purposes and in a variety of situations.

For each volume in this guide, there is a short narrative of our rationale for cross-referencing. The subject matter of some of the activities does not lend itself well for use in another context but we believe you find a high degree of transferability. At the end of many volume chapters (or parts) of the nine Wiley texts examined in this guide, there is a short statement suggesting one or more activities in other chapters of other volumes that also focus on a related concept or region. This cross-referencing of materials is meant to save the instructor time and to maximize the degree of attention that might be devoted to a particular subject, concept, country or region.

For example, discussion of the rank-size regularity (or its opposite, the primate city distribution) appears

315

in two of the nine parts of this *Activity Guide*. It is discussed in *Part 10: The Urbanizing World* of deBlij's *Human Geography: Culture, Society and Space* (hereafter referred to as deBlij). It is also the focus of the activity to accompany *Chapter 6: Urban Geography* of the volume edited by Berentsen entitled *Contemporary Europe: A Geographical Analysis* (hereafter referred to as Berentsen).

Similarly, if the instructor's focus is on central place theory, there are two activities that focus on that topic. The nature of the settlement system in the classic central place testing ground of Iowa is the activity developed to accompany *Chapter 9: Take Me Out to the Ball Game: Market Areas and the Urban Hierarchy* in the new interactive human geography book written by Kuby, et al. entitled *Human Geography in Action* (hereafter referred to as Kuby). For those wishing to focus on the more practical and applied aspects of city distribution and central place theory, there is the measurement of actual distances among central places in the Zuider Zee reclamation area of the Netherlands. That activity appears in *Chapter 8: The Location of Tertiary Activities* in Wheeler, *et al. Economic Geography*, 2nd edition (hereafter referred to as Wheeler). Activities that can be cross-referenced to give the instructor more freedom of choice in the supplemental materials that he or she might assign to his or her students.

What follows is a volume-by-volume narrative of the chapters (or parts) of other of the nine Wiley texts examined that might be considered supplemental or complementary to the chapter (or part) listed.

Volume: Harm J. deBlij and Peter O. Muller, *Geography: Realms, Regions and Concepts*, *Eighth Edition* (New York: John Wiley and Sons, 1997).

Introduction in deBlij and Muller *World Regional Geography: Physical and Human Foundations*. The focus of the activity ("*Back in the USSR: Georgia on My Mind*") is on a trouble spot in the Transcaucausus where bitter ethnic and religious tensions are evident. Likewise, the activity that accompanies **Chapter 2 in Berentsen** Physical Geography has to do with the beautiful Dinaric Alps an area in the Balkans also subject to competing territorial claims ("*Alpine for You*").

Chapter 1 in deBlij and Muller *Resilient Europe: Confronting New Challenges*. The activity focuses on the classical theory of agricultural land use put forward by von Thünen and its more contemporary macro-Thünen derivatives ("*Von Thünen of Whole Wheat? Contemporary European Agricultural Land Use*"). **Chapter 13 in Wheeler** *The Spatial Organization of Agriculture* also focuses on this same important subject. In this case, the activity examines the spatial distribution of large-scale commercial farming in the United States ("*'Real' Agriculture: Implosion or Explosion?*").

Chapter 2 in deBlij and Muller *Russia's Fractious Federation*. The purpose of the activity associated with this chapter ("*Siberia: Many Rivers Run Through It*") is to provide the student with a virtual field trip through this expansive and often desolate landscape. Likewise, **Exercise 1 in the Physical**

triad *The Earth as a Rotating Planet* includes an activity that examines time zones around the world with particular emphasis on the vastness of Siberia and the many time zones it includes (*"Zoning in on Greenwich: Giving You the Time of Day"*).

Chapter 3 in deBlij and Muller *North America: The Postindustrial Transformation* is quite broad in scope. The activity chosen focuses on two separatist movements in culturally pluralistic Canada (*"Uh Oh, Canada: A Fractured Federal Tale"*). For a more in-depth examination of Canada's long-term climate change the student might be referred to the activity that accompanies **Exercise 2 in the Physical** *books The Global Energy System* ("*There's a Hole, There's a Hole, There's a Hole at the Bottom of the World: Ozone Depletion in Antarctica*")

Chapter 4 in deBlij and Muller *Middle America: Collision of Cultures* examines many collisions but the one of interest in the activity is the physical collision of crustal plates that cause seismic activity throughout the region ("*The Land of Shake and Bake: Landscapes of Earthquakes and Volcanoes in Mexico*"). The theory of continental drift is explored more in depth in the activity that accompanies **Exercise 9 of the Physical** books *Lithosphere and Tectonics* ("*Continental Blue Plate Special: Fetuccine Alfredo Wegener*").

Chapter 5 in deBlij and Muller *South America: Continent of* Contrasts. The topic of the activity is a virtual fieldtrip to the rainforest of Suriname and the development potential of such a fragile ecosystem.

Preserving the rainforest, distributing land holdings more equitably and alleviating poverty in urban and rural Latin America are the subjects of the activity meant to accompany **Chapter 14 in Blouet** *Latin America and the World Scene* (*"Banking on the Future of Latin America: Solving Rural Poverty"*).

Chapter 6 in deBlij and Muller *North Africa/Southwest Asia: The Energy of Islam.* The activity examines the plight of a stateless nation (the Kurds) in the Middle East. The political is one of many facets of life in the Middle East. **Part 2 of deBlij** *Population and Space* deals with the vast difference between arithmetic and physiologic density in Egypt and other Middle Eastern nations that contain vast amounts of desert (*'You Are My Density"*).

Chapter 7 in deBlij and Muller *Subsaharan Africa: Realm of Reversals*. The purist may be upset that the focus of the activity that accompanies this chapter focuses on Tombouctou (Timbuktu) in Mali which is technically not in Subsaharan Africa, but rather in the Sahel. The activity focuses on ancient Timbuktu when it was, in fact, part of a Subsaharan kingdom. Two other activities that do focus on Subsaharan Africa include that found in **Part 7 of deBlij** *Patterns of Language* (*"You Are What You Speak: African Lingua Francae"*) and that in **Chapter 11 of Wheeler** *Manufacturing: Regional Patterns and Problems* that focuses, in part, on Botswana (*"Diamonds in the Rough: Facets of Industrial Development"*).

Chapter 9 in deBlij and Muller *East Asia: Realm of Titans*. The activity accompanying this chapter is a focus on the burgeoning city and enterprise zone of Shanghai. A good complement to this urban focus would be to assign the activity associated with **Exercise 15 in the Physical** books *The Work of Waves and Wind* . The activity ("*Loess is More*") examines the fertility of the loessal plains of China and their importance for Chinese agriculture both historically and currently.

Chapter 10 in deBlij and Muller *Southeast Asia: Between the Giants*. The activity associated with this chapter has to do with the beautiful, backward and inward-looking country of Mynamar (formerly Burma). Another theme that might be pursued in Southeast Asia (and beyond) is the influence of the Chinese Diaspora on the economy of the entire region. **Part 12 of deBlij** *The Political Imprint* contains an activity that focuses specifically on the overseas Chinese who escaped from Hong Kong before the Chinese takeover in July 1997 ("*The Yacht Sea People: Roll the Dice and End Up in Vancouver*").

Chapter 11 in deBlij and Muller *Australia: Dilemmas Downunder*. Australia is also alluded to in an activity to accompany **Chapter 3 of Kuby** *Tracking the AIDS Epidemic: Diffusion Through Time and Space*. One of the three Chinatowns discussed in "*Digging to Chinatown: Relocation Diffusion in Action*" is that of Sydney, Australia.

Chapter 12 in deBlij and Muller *The Pacific Realm: Uncertain Futures.* Another activity that focuses on Micronesia and Fijian culture is found in **Chapter 5 of the Physical** texts *Winds and the Global Circulation System.* The activity ("*A World Wind Tour*") focuses on the importance of sailing winds to the peoples of the South Pacific.

Volume: Harm J. deBlij, *Human Geography: Culture, Society, and Space, Fifth Edition* (New York: John Wiley and Sons, Inc., 1996).

Part 1 in deBlij *Environment and Humanity* is a broad subject area. The activity focuses on a small section of the chapter dealing with revealed residential desirability via mental mapping ("*Rocky Mountain High (and Corn Belt Low)*"). A broader perspective might be found in **Chapter 5 of Kuby** *Trapped in Space: Space-Time Prisms and Individual Activity Space.* The accompanying activity ("*My Prism can be my Prison*") allows the student to work with the concepts of time-geography as discussed by Törsten Hägerstränd and his associates.

Part 2 in deBlij *Population and Space* is another multi-faceted subject area. The activity in the book focuses on differing measures of population density ("*You are my Density*"). Another important aspect of population is the age-sex cohort (i.e., the population "pyramid") is the focus of the activity in **Chapter 7 of Kuby** *The Hidden Momentum of Population Growth.* The activity focuses specifically on Egypt ("*Another Type of Egyptian Pyramid*").

321

Part 3 in deBlij *Streams of Human Mobility* is an examination of migration throughout the world. The activity that accompanies the chapter ("*Like Salmon Swimming Upstream?*") focuses on African-American migration (and subsequent counter migration) in the United States. For a broader perspective, you might also use the activity that accompanies **Chapter 5 in Blouet** *Population: Growth, Distribution, and Migration* entitled "*Why you have to go to New York City to get your Go-Go Boots Shined: Brazilians on the Move*" which refers to the most common job titles held by Brazilians migrating to New York City.

Part 4 in deBlij *Patterns of Nutrition and Health* can be tied into the activity that accompanies **Wheeler Chapter 2** *Global Population Processes and Pressures* entitled "*Painting the World by Numbers*". A whole series of demographic and public health variables are examined.

Part 5 in deBlij *Geography and Inequality* can be reinforced by assigning the activity contained in **Kuby Chapter 12** ("*Timor or Less: Indonesia's Claim at Stake*") that focuses in part on gender issues in beleaguered Timor.

Part 6 in deBlij *Landscape and the Geography of Culture* can be embellished by having the students examine the activities associated with the **Introductory chapter in deBlij and Muller** *("Back in the USSR: Georgia on my Mind*") and/or **Chapter 3 in Berentsen** ("*A Grecian Formula for Population? The Graying of Europe*"). Both activities focus at least in part on the nature of ethnically diverse and fragmented areas such as the Transcaucasus and the Balkans.

Part 7 in deBlij *Patterns of Language* is a fascinating subject. The activity in deBlij focuses on the language of business and trade in Africa ("*You Are What you Speak: African Lingua Francae*"). The focus of **Chapter 12 in deBlij and Muller** is on languages too, but this time those of the South Pacific *("Want to Know Samoa? Read On!"*).

Part 8 in deBlij *Geography of Religion* is quite broad. The activity to accompany that chapter is more directly focused on the variability of religious expression within the rubric of Christianity. Even more focused is the activity to accompany **Chapter 11 in Kuby** *Do Orange and Green Clash? Residential Segregation in Northern Ireland* on the religious conflicts between Catholic and Protestant in Northern Ireland ("*I'll see your Bernadette Devlin and Raise you an Ian Paisley*").

Part 9 in deBlij *Cultural Landscapes of Farming* can encompass anything from subsistence farming by small-plot cultivators to commercial agro-business enterprises on a grand scale. The activity in deBlij ("*Let them eat Jute: The Colonial Legacy in World Agriculture*") focuses on peasant farmers in Bangladesh. On the other hand, the activity that accompanies **Chapter 13 in Wheeler** *The Spatial Organization of Agriculture* ("'Real' Agriculture: Implosion or Explosion?") focuses on modern commercial agriculture in the United States.

Part 10 in deBlij *The Urbanizing World* can be related to several other activities in other books including the activity included with **Berentsen Chapter 6** ("*How Did Brussels Sprout? Urbanization in Belgium*") and that included with **Kuby Chapter 9** ("*Towns in Iowa: Central Places and a Whole Lot More!*").

Part 11 in deBlij *Cultures, Landscapes and Regions of Industry* contains an activity that focuses mainly on the maquiladoras in the Tijuana-San Diego area. For complete coverage, the instructor is encouraged to consider assigning the activity accompanying **Chapter 10 in Wheeler** *Manufacturing: Where Plants Locate and Why* as well ("*Run for the Border: NAFTA*").

Part 12 in deBlij *The Political Imprint* discusses the recent Hong Kong Diaspora prior to the takeover of the former British colony by China. Their impact has been especially felt in Vancouver. Likewise, **Chapter 3 in Kuby** *Tracking the AIDS Epidemic: Diffusion Through Time and Space*, despite the chapter title, contains an activity that is closely related to that in **Part 12 of deBlij**. The activity is entitled "*Digging to Chinatown: Relocation Diffusion in Action*". The Vancouver Chinatown is one of three that the activity focuses on.

Volume: Michael Kuby, John Harner and Patricia Gober, *Human Geography in Action* (New York: John Wiley and Sons, Inc., 1998).

Chapter 1 in Kuby *True Maps, False Impressions: Making, Manipulating, and Interpreting Maps* examines the whole of cartography. The accompanying activity ("*Large Map, Small Scale; Small Map, Large Scale*") focuses on the concept of map scale whereas the activity designed to accompany **Part 1 of deBlij** Environment and Humanity examines the relevant area of mental mapping ("*Rocky Mountain High (and Corn Belt Low)*").

Chapter 2 in Kuby *Cactus, Cowboys, and Coyotes: The Southwest Culture Region* examines how cultural stereotypes evolve and are maintained. Maintaining identity in a culturally pluralistic society is the related concept examined in the activity that accompanies **Chapter 3 in deBlij and Muller** *North America: The Postindustrial Transformation.* The activity is entitled "*Uh Oh, Canada: A Fractured Federal Tale.*"

Chapter 3 in Kuby *Tracking the AIDS Epidemic: Diffusion Through Space and Time* examines the epidemiology of our modern scourge on humanity. Migrations can also be studied using the same diffusion mechanisms and the student might which to extend the overseas Chinese focus of the activity to other realms. The exercise that accompanies **Chapter 5 in Blouet** *Population: Growth, Distribution, and Migration* discusses recent Brazilian migrations into New York City ("*Why you have to go to New York City to get your Go-Go Boots Shined: Brazilians on the Move*").

Chapter 4 in Kuby *Newton's First Law of Migration: The Gravity Model* extols the virtues of natural laws to explain aggregate behavior. If the instructor wishes to emphasize other applications of geographic location theory, he or she might wish to assign the activity to accompany **Chapter 8 of Wheeler** *The Location of Tertiary Activities.* The activity is entitled "*Here's the Rub: The Dutch have to Modify Central Place Spacing*".

Chapter 5 in Kuby *Trapped in Space: Space-Time Prisms and Individual Activity Space* should have students wondering about the role of transportation in causing the time-space convergence they continue to experience. Another venue that considers this issue is **Chapter 3 in Wheeler** *Global Economic Development.* The activity is entitled "*Thumbs Down: A Hitchhiker's Guide to the Globe*" and it should reinforce the uneven nature of personal transportation availability throughout the world.

Chapter 6 in Kuby *Help Wanted: The Changing Geography of Jobs* contains an activity that compares the economic base of countries a variety of development levels. The country that has the highest percentage of its employment in manufacturing is Botswana. The incredulous student (and instructor) might wish to pursue this further by examining the activity that accompanies **Chapter 11 in *Wheeler*** *Manufacturing: Regional Patterns and Problems.* The title of the activity is "*Diamonds in the Rough: Facets of Industrial Development* " that might indicate why Botswana is the world's leading manufacturer (as measured by percentage of the gainfully employed labor force in that sector).

Chapter 7 in Kuby *The Hidden Momentum of Population Growth* contains an activity that focuses largely on Egypt ("*Another Type of Egyptian Pyramid*"). For the instructor who might wish to intensify this Egyptian focus, we would suggest **Part 2 in deBlij** *Population and Space*. The accompanying activity ("*You are my Density*") examines the difference between arithmetic and physiologic density that is greatest in Egypt.

Chapter 8 in Kuby *From Rags to Riches: The Dimensions of Development* might be cross-referenced with any number of activities in other books. Two that stand out are **Chapter 4 in Wheeler** *The Interdependent Global Economy* with an activity that focuses on banking in a third world context ("*Banking on Technology*") and **Chapter 1 in Berentsen** *Introduction*. The activity here focuses on the developed portion of the world specifically the origins and future of the European Union and its common currency ("*From Steel Girders to Fiber Optics: Origins of the European Union*"). The contrast in development levels is a theme that can be found in other chapters, too. We'd be interested in finding out which of the activities works best for the instructor and resonates most with the students.

Chapter 9 in Kuby *Take Me Out to the Ball Game: Market Areas and the Urban Hierarchy* is a great example of applied location theory especially the elements of central place theory. As fully-articulated central place hierarchies are supposed to be rank-size, any discussion of the interrelationship between central place theory and the rank-size rule should focus on the activity contained in **Chapter 6 of Berentsen** *Urban Geography* entitled "*How did Brussels Sprout? Urbanization in Belgium*". The hyperurbanization of Belgium and the rank-size regularity form the basis for the activity.

Chapter 10 in Kuby *Reading the Urban Landscape Through Census Data and Field Observation* addresses an important aspect of urban geography—empirical field work. The activity for this chapter, "*Manhattan Transformation: The Suburban Roots of Harlem*", has the student thinking backwards about what a central city area today might have been like when it was a suburb on the periphery of an expanding metropolitan region. An activity that has students speculating about the urban future is found in **Chapter 7 of Wheeler** *The City as an Economic Node*. *The City* has the students focus on Houston--the city in Texas best known for having its fortunes tuned to the health of the "oil patch" economy and for having no zoning regulations ("*Houston, We Have a Problem: Invasion of the Multiple Nuclei*"). The students should speculate about urban sprawl and land use planning.

Chapter 11 in Kuby *Do Orange and Green Clash? Residential Segregation in Northern Ireland* deals with religiously based conflict in Northern Ireland. The student might also examine the activity in **Part 8 of deBlij** *Geography of Religion* entitled *Christianity Worldwide: Plain Vanilla or 31 Flavors*?"

Chapter 12 in Kuby *The Rise of Nationalism and the Fall of Yugoslavia* examines the tragedy of the Balkans. The associated activity looks at another neo-colonial nationalistic clash that receives less attention in North America—the Indonesian claims to Timor (*"Timor or Less: Indonesia's Claim at Stake"*). A good companion activity is the one associated with **Part 5 of deBlij** *Geography and Inequality* that focuses on inequality in gender roles around the world (*" A Woman's Place is in the House…and in the Senate"*).

Volume: The triad of Physical Geography textbooks that include: Alan Strahler and Arthur Strahler, *Physical Geography: Science and Systems of the Human Environment* (New York: John Wiley and Sons, Inc., 1997); Alan Strahler and Arthur Strahler, *Introducing Physical Geography, Second Edition* (New York: John Wiley and Sons, 1998); and Harm J. deBlij and Peter O. Muller, *Physical Geography of the Global Environment* (New York: John Wiley and Sons, 1997).

Exercise 1 in Physical *The Earth as a Rotating Planet* contains an activity dealing with time zones with an emphasis on the immense size of Russia, especially Siberia. Siberia is also discussed in **Chapter 2 of deBlij and Muller** *Russia's Fractious Federation* in the activity *entitled "Siberia: Many Rivers Run Through It"*.

Exercise 4 in Physical *Atmospheric Moisture and Precipitation* develops an activity entitled "*Somewhere over the Rain Shadow*". The orographic effect is one cause of desert or steppe-like conditions on the rain shadow side. Other mechanisms are discussed in a focus on the Atacama Desert of Chile in **Chapter 2 of Blouet** *Physical Environments of Latin America.* The related activity is entitled "*Where Not to Be in Raincoat Sales: High and Dry in the Atacama Desert*".

Exercise 5 in Physical *Winds and the Global Circulation System* examines wind patterns around the world including the tropics. For a more in-depth look at how the wind and weather patterns in some of these exotic tropical locales affects the tourist trade see **Chapter 8 in Kuby** *From Rags to Riches: The Dimensions of Development.* The emphasis of the activity is on the emerging niche market for ecotourism ("*Ecotourism: It Isn't Easy Being Green—But it Can be Profitable*").

Exercise 7 in Physical *The Global Scope of Climate; Low-Latitude Climates; Midlatitude and High-Latitude Climates* explores the Koeppen classification system. The relationship between climate and human behavior has been a hotly debated topic for millennia. In the early part of this century the theoretical constructs of environmental determinism mesmerized the field of geography (and many others as well). That "theory" is the focus of the activity representing **Part 6 of deBlij** *Landscape and the Geography of Culture* entitled "*What'll it be?: Lethargic and Clever or Vigorous and Stupid?*"

Exercise 8 in Physical *Earth Materials and the Cycle of Rock Change* presents the three different classes of rocks and their geological origins. For an application of the geology lesson, the student might find **Chapter 4 of deBlij and Muller** *Middle America: Collision of Cultures* of interest. The exercise developed for that chapter emphasizes two tectonic processes affecting the landscape of Mexico City ("*The Land of Shake and Bake: Landscapes of Earthquakes and Volcanoes in Mexico*").

Exercise 9 in Physical *Lithosphere and Tectonics* is technical and so is the activity developed for it ("*Continental Blue Plate Special: Fetuccine Alfredo Wegener*"). If the student wants a more humanistic perspective on how the physical environment created by such tectonic activity affects the daily lives of the people who live in these extreme environments, see **Chapter 11 in Blouet** *Andean America* and the activity entitled "Mountains of Potatoes: The Nature and Cultures of the Andes".

Exercise 10 in Physical *Volcanic and Tectonic Landforms*. The texts do an excellent job of explaining the rudiments of volcanism and the accompanying activity ("*Return to Cinder*") is meant to bring that learning closer to home by focusing on an event that every college student in the United States remembers—the 1980 explosion of Mount St. Helens in Washington. Volcanoes, especially when they are inactive, also make for fascinating landscapes as pointed out in the activity developed to accompany **Chapter 10 in Blouet** *The West Indies* entitled "*Volcanoes in the Lesser Antilles: Hot Times in the Islands*".

Exercise 12 in Physical *The Cycling of Water on the Continents* is a complex chapter and the activity ("*'Mites Go Up, 'Tites Come Down: Karst Sinkholes and Caves*") was designed solely to focus on karst topography in western Kentucky. **Chapter 2 in Berentsen** *Physical Geography* focuses on the Dinaric Alps, another karst landscape in an activity entitled "*Alpine for You*"

Exercise 13 in Physical *Fluvial Processes and Landforms* covers a variety of water-related topics but spectacular waterfalls hold a special interest for residents and tourists alike and form the basis of the activity ("*Wet and Wild Waterfalls*"). Another activity that picks up on the theme of turning natural attractions such as waterfalls into tourist amenities is **Chapter 8 in Kuby** on ecotourism. The activity is entitled "*Ecotourism: It's Not Easy Being Green--But it can be Profitable*".

Exercise 15 in Physical *Glacier Systems and the Ice Age* focuses on an area in southwestern Wisconsin and portions of Iowa and Illinois that were missed by the most recent glacial period. This so-called Driftless Area forms the basis for the activity "*The Iceman Misseth: Implications for the Driftless Area*". **Chapter 9 in Kuby** *Take Me Out to the Ball Game: Market Areas and the Urban Hierarchy* also focuses on the central place system in Iowa, the northeastern part of which is included in the Driftless Area. That physical factor may partially explain the spacing of settlements in that quadrant of the state, the focus of the chapter activity "*Towns in Iowa: Central Places and a Whole Lot More!*".

Exercise 17 in Physical *Soil Systems* examines among other things the phenomenon of desertification, especially in the Sahel of Africa. Another substantive study that focuses on climatic changes in this part of the world is found in **Chapter 7 of deBlij and Muller** *Subsaharan Africa: Realm of Reversals*. The accompanying exercise focuses on the shifting fortunes of Tombouctou (i.e., Timbuktu) in present-day Mali. During the Middle Ages, Timbuktu was one of the richest trade centers on earth and the jewel in the crown of the Empire of Ghana to the south ("One Hump or Two? Overland Trade Routes to Timbuktu").

Exercise 18 in Physical *Systems and Cycles of the Biosphere and Global Ecosystems* is one of those sweeping catch-all chapters that tries to focus on ecological imbalances planet-wide. The activity designed to go along with this chapter is also encouraging the reader to become proactive about ecological issues of concern to them within their locales ("*Act Locally, Think Globally*"). Global sustainability, especially the alarming rate of animal and plant extinctions, is also the subject of **Chapter 13 in *Kuby*** *Human Impact on the Environment*. The activity entitled "*How Would You Like Your Animals—Rare? Vacancies at the World Zoo*" is a good complement to the physical exercise.

Volume: James O. Wheeler, Peter O. Muller, Grant Ian Thrall and Timothy J. Fik, *Economic Geography*, Third Edition (New York: John Wiley and Sons, Inc., 1998).

Chapter 1 in Wheeler *The Study of Economic Geography* is an overview of many concepts used in economic geography. The activity associated with the chapter ("*One Picture Tells a Thousand Geographies*") focuses on the book cover photograph which so ironically captures elements of the traditional and modern simultaneously. A related activity might be found in **Chapter 2 of deBlij and Muller** *Russia's Fractious Federation.* That activity ("*Siberia: Many Rivers Run Through It*") attempts to put a human face on a region that is supposedly filled with emptiness, loneliness and depression. The student should come away somewhat disabused of that notion.

Chapter 2 in Wheeler *Global Population Processes and Pressures* The activity for this chapter examines many of the population/demographic statistics available on *Encarta Virtual Globe CD-ROM.* A more focused look at population density can be found in the activity designed to accompany **Part 2 of deBlij** *Population and Space.* That activity is entitled "*You Are My Density*".

Chapter 3 in Wheeler *Global Economic Development.* The activity associated with this chapter examines the vast disparities between those countries that have reasonable access to private means of transportation and those who do not. A complementary activity would be the one designed to accompany **Chapter 5 in Kuby** *Trapped in Space: Space-Time Prisms and Individual Activity Space.* It is entitled "*My Prism Can be my Prison*" and helps to illustrate the concept of the time-space convergence so crucial to an understanding of advances in transportation technology.

Chapter 4 in Wheeler *The Interdependent Global Economy.* Global interdependence and global capitalism is an awfully large subject to embrace in a single activity. The one on banking in Wheeler ("*Banking on Technology*") might be complemented by that in **Chapter 1 of Berentsen**. *Introduction.* The manner in which the skids are being greased for a smooth transition to a single European currency (the Euro) is the focus of the activity ("*From Steel Girders to Fiber Optics: Origins of the European Union*").

Chapter 5 in Wheeler *Principles of Spatial Interaction.* The activity designed to accompany this chapter deals with the stage model of transportation development first discussed by Taaffe, Morrill and Gould ("*Geography is Very Spatial to Me!*"). A good complement to the contemporary focus on transportation systems within different states of the United States is found in the activity associated with **Chapter 3 of Blouet** *Aboriginal and Colonial Geography of Latin America* ("*Trail of Years: Historical Linkages Along the Inca Highway*").

Chapter 6 in Wheeler *The Role of Transportation in Economic Geography.* The activity here is an historic look at the relatively short-lived canal building craze in the United States. In addition, you might wish to examine an exotic, albeit modern means of transportation aboard the Trans-Siberian Railway by doing the activity suggested in **Chapter 2 of deBlij and Muller** *Russia's Fractious Federation* ("*Siberia: Many Rivers Run Through It*").

Chapter 7 in Wheeler *The City as an Economic Node.* It might be interesting to compare and contrast the urban evolution of Houston, Texas a city that can annex surrounding suburban territory easily and for which zoning is mostly an afterthought with more "typical" suburban development. The activity associated with **Chapter 10 in Kuby** *Reading the Urban Landscape Through Census Data and Field Observation* ("*Manhattan Transformation: The Suburban Roots of Harlem*") compares Harlem's transition from early suburb of New York to modern inner-city ethnic neighborhood with King of Prussia, Pennsylvania that began as a dormitory suburb of Philadelphia and grew into a suburban downtown node of activity.

Chapter 8 in Wheeler *The Location of Tertiary Activities.* The activity for this chapter discusses the spacing of settlements developed *de novo* from the reclaimed polderland in the Netherlands. Location theory is not immutable as the Dutch found out when they tried to hew too closely to the Christaller version of the theory thirty years after it was developed. The perfect complement to this activity is the one that accompanies **Chapter 9 in Kuby** *Take Me Out to the Ball Game: Market Areas and the Urban Hierarchy*. The activity (*"Towns in Iowa: Central Places and a Whole Lot More!"*) has the student measure nearest neighbor distances among central places of high order in the state of Iowa, the classic central place testing ground. The results of the comparison with the Netherlands (and thus southern Germany) are startling.

Chapter 9 in Wheeler *The Changing Economic Geography of the Restructured Metropolis*. The activity accompanying this chapter ("A Tale of Three Cities") examines New Orleans, Denver and Baltimore and what they've given up to their surrounding suburbs. A good contrast might be to examine planned communities that did not just grow with no rhyme or reason. The activity accompanying **Chapter 7 in Berentsen** *The British Isles* (*"Planning the Garden Cities of Tomorrow: Avoiding Urban Anarchy in the UK"*) does just that. New towns based on the urban vision of Ebenezer Howard are showcased.

Chapter 10 in Wheeler *Manufacturing: Where Plants Locate and Why*. The activity in this chapter focuses on maquiladora plants in the Cuidad Juarez-El Paso area (*"Run for the Border: NAFTA"*). It is fitting students might also be assigned to complete the activity associated with **Part 11 of deBlij** *Cultures, Landscapes, and Regions of Industry*. That activity (*"Maquiladora? Is that the Latest Latin Dance Craze?"*) focuses mainly on the San Diego-Tijuana area of the US-Mexican border.

Chapter 11 in Wheeler *Manufacturing: Regional Patterns and Problems*. The activity here focuses mainly on mining in Botswana, the country with the highest proportion of its labor force in manufacturing. Activities in two other chapters are related and might also be assigned. The first is **Chapter 7 in Blouet** *Mining, Manufacturing and Services*. The activity here ("*Tin Men and Women: Mining in Bolivia*") might be compared to a mineral economy in Botswana based on diamond extraction. The second activity is found in **Chapter 6 of Kuby** *Help Wanted: The Changing Geography of Jobs*. The activity ("*Around the World from Pre- to Post-Industrial*") has the student examine the employment profile of five disparate countries at various stages on the continuum of economic development.

Chapter 12 in Wheeler *The Economic Geography of Energy*. The activity in the chapter focuses on a relatively unusual form of renewable energy in the form of geothermal power. The activity corresponding to **Chapter 5 in Berentsen** *Economic Geography* entitled "*Oil and Water DO Mix: Petroleum Reserves in the North Sea*" might also be used. It focuses on the geopolitical and economic issues facing the countries that are blessed with an abundance of oil and natural gas within their sector of the North Sea submerged beds.

Chapter 13 in Wheeler *The Spatial Organization of Agriculture*. The activity associated with this chapter updates Hart's concept of 'real' agriculture using more recent data from the agricultural census. It is probably wise to also assign the activity associated with **Chapter 1 in deBlij and Muller** *Resilient Europe: Confronting New Challenges*. That activity ("*von Thünen on Whole Wheat? Contemporary European Agricultural Land Use*") tests to determine whether macro-Thünen models have any relevance in explaining modern European agricultural land use patterns.

Chapter 14 in Wheeler *Contemporary American Agriculture: Regions and Trends*. The activity in this chapter focuses on the commercial dairy belt in the United States. The instructor may wish to contrast commercial agriculture in the United States, which is really big business, with small plot cultivation in the third world. A good activity for this would be that which accompanies **Part 9 of deBlij** *Cultural Landscapes of Farming* entitled "*Let Them Eat Jute: The Colonial Legacy in World Agriculture*". This activity examines the disastrous consequences of a saturated world market for a commercial cash crop such as jute, the commercial staple of Bangladesh.

Volume: William H. Berentsen, ed., *Contemporary Europe: A Geographic Analysis Seventh Edition* (New York: John Wiley and Sons, Inc., 1997).

Chapter 2 in Berentsen: *Physical Geography* can be related to **Wheeler Chapter 8** *The Location of Tertiary Activities* (activity entitled "*Here's the Rub: The Dutch Have to Modify Central Place Spacing*"). The emphasis of the activity developed for Berentsen is the mountainous portions of Europe, whereas the activity in Wheeler, *et al.* focuses on the flat northern European plain.

Chapter 3 in Berentsen: *Population* can complement **deBlij Part 2** *Population and Space.* The activity entitled "*You are my Density*" focuses, in part, on arithmetic and physiologic density levels in the Netherlands.

Chapter 5 in Berentsen: *Economic Geography* deals with one form of extractive industry (the mining of petroleum and natural gas from the North Sea) and the activity in **deBlij and Muller Chapter 1** *Resilient Europe: Confronting New Challenges* (entitled "*von Thünen on Whole Wheat? Contemporary European Agricultural Land Use*") focuses on another--agriculture.

Chapter 6 in Berentsen: *Urban Geography* can be related to the activity designed to accompany **deBlij Part 8** *Geography of Religion.* The activity, entitled "*Christianity Worldwide: Plain Vanilla or 31 Flavors?*" focuses in part on the culture divide between the Huguenots and the Walloons in Belgium. The activity in **Chapter 6 of Berentsen** ("*How did Brussels Sprout? Urbanization in Belgium*") focuses on the importance of Brussels within the Belgian urban system.

Chapter 7 in Berentsen: *The British Isles* might profitably draw upon the activity included in **Kuby Chapter 11:***Do Orange and Green Clash?: Residential Segregation in Northern Ireland. "I'll See your Bernadette Devlin and Raise you an Ian*

340

Paisley" focuses on the recent peace accord to end the "Troubles" in Northern Ireland. Ethnic neighborhoods in Northern Ireland could be contrasted to the new town developments in England which is the focus of the activity in Berentsen *("Planting the Garden Cities of Tomorrow: Avoiding Urban Anarchy in the UK*").

Chapter 9 in Berentsen: *Region Nord: The European North* focuses on the Faeroes whereas the activity to Chapter 12 in **Wheeler,** *The Economic Geography of Energy* focuses on the innovative use of geothermal energy in Iceland. The activity is entitled "*Hot Under the Crust: Geothermal Energy in Iceland*."

Chapter 11 in Berentsen: *West Central Europe* focuses almost exclusively on the reunification of Germany after the fall of the Berlin Wall in 1989. To extend the examination of west central Europe it might be interesting to examine **Wheeler Chapter 11** *Manufacturing: Regional Patterns and Problems* which focuses in part on the role of manufacturing in Switzerland's economic base. The activity is entitled "*Diamond in the Rough: Facets of Industrial Development*".

Chapter 12 in Berentsen: *East Central and Southeastern Europe* focuses on the Jewish ghetto in Krakow and the devastating impact of the Holocaust on Poland. Poland is also featured in the activity to accompany **Chapter 18 of the Physical Geography** triad *(Systems and Cycles of the Biosphere and Global Ecosystems)*. The activity ("*Act Locally,*

Think Globally") focuses in part on the last remaining old growth lowland temperate forest in Europe which straddles the Poland-Belarus border. Also, the activity for **Part 8 of deBlij's** *Geography of Religion* ("*Christianity Worldwide: Plain Vanilla or 31 Flavors?*") focuses some attention on Roman Catholicism in Poland and the Orthodox Church in Bulgaria.

Chapter 13 in Berentsen: *Russia and the European NIS* . The subject matter that might be covered here is enormous. The activity in Berentsen ("*Unhappily Ever After?*") focuses on the soaring divorce rate in the Baltic Republics. Other activities that involve Russia or the European NIS include that which accompanies the **Introductory Chapter of deBlij and Muller** ("*Back in the USSR: Georgia on my Mind*"). The activity focuses on struggles in the Transcaucasus region. **Chapter 1 in the Physical Geography** involves an activity ("*Zoning in on Greenwich: Giving you the Time of Day*") that makes the student aware of the vastness of Siberia and the number of time zones there are in Russia.

Volume: Brian W. Blouet and Olwyn M. Blouet, *Latin America and the Caribbean: A Systematic and Regional Survey* (New York: John Wiley and Sons, Inc., 1997).

Chapter 6 in Blouet *The Latin American City* can be linked to **deBlij and Muller** *Regional* **Chapter 4** *Middle America: Collision of Cultures* (activity entitled *The Land of Shake and Bake: Landscapes of Earthquakes and Volcanoes in Mexico*) This activity focuses specifically on the devastating earthquake in 1985 and why Mexico City is qo vulnerable to seismic aativity which complementq the material on the urban spatial structure of Mexico City as an illustration of the Griffin-Ford model in the Blouet chapter.

Chapter 12 in Blouet: *Brazil* can be linked to **Kuby Chapter 6** *Help Wanted: The Changing Geography of Jobs* (activity entitled *Around the World from Pre- to Post-Industrial*). Brazil, as a newly industrializing country (NIC), is one of several used to illustrate differences in economic development levels and can be related to the Blouet activity on the development of Brasilia and the interior since the 1960s.

Chapter 14 in Blouet: *Latin America and the World Scene* can be linked to both **Wheeler Chapter 10** *Manufacturing: Where Plants Locate and Why* (activity entitled "*Run for the Border: NAFTA*") and to **deBlij Part 11** *Cultures, Landscapes, and Regions of Industry* (activity entitled "*Maquiladora? Is That the Latest Latin Dance Craze?*"). Both of the ancillary activities deal with Maquiladora plants although the former focuses attention more on the El Paso-Ciudad Juarez area and the latter on the San Diego-Tijuana area.

NOTES

NOTES

NOTES

NOTES

NOTES

NOTES